BRIDGES®
IN MATHEMATICS

SECOND EDITION
HOME CONNECTIONS

GRADE
1

Published by The **MATH LEARNING CENTER** Salem, Oregon

Bridges in Mathematics Second Edition Grade 1 Home Connections

The Bridges in Mathematics Grade 1 package consists of:

Bridges in Mathematics Grade 1 Teachers Guide Units 1–8

Bridges in Mathematics Grade 1 Assessment Guide

Bridges in Mathematics Grade 1 Teacher Masters

Bridges in Mathematics Grade 1 Student Book

Bridges in Mathematics Grade 1 Home Connections

Bridges in Mathematics Grade 1 Teacher Masters Answer Key

Bridges in Mathematics Grade 1 Student Book Answer Key

Bridges in Mathematics Grade 1 Home Connections Answer Key

Bridges in Mathematics Grade 1 Components & Manipulatives

Bridges Educator Site

Work Place Games & Activities

Number Corner Grade 1 Teachers Guide Volumes 1–3

Number Corner Grade 1 Teacher Masters

Number Corner Grade 1 Student Book

Number Corner Grade 1 Teacher Masters Answer Key

Number Corner Grade 1 Student Book Answer Key

Number Corner Grade 1 Components & Manipulatives

Word Resource Cards

Digital resources noted in italics.

The Math Learning Center, PO Box 12929, Salem, Oregon 97309. Tel 1 (800) 575-8130
www.mathlearningcenter.org

Prepared for publication using Mac OS X and Adobe Creative Suite.
Printed in the United States of America.

To reorder Home Connections, refer to number 2B1HC5 (package of 5 sets).

QBB1903
Updated 2019-05-29.

Bridges in Mathematics is a standards-based K–5 curriculum that provides a unique blend of concept development and skills practice in the context of problem solving. It incorporates Number Corner, a collection of daily skill-building activities for students.

The Math Learning Center is a nonprofit organization serving the education community. Our mission is to inspire and enable individuals to discover and develop their mathematical confidence and ability. We offer innovative and standards-based professional development, curriculum, materials, and resources to support learning and teaching. To find out more, visit us at www.mathlearningcenter.org.

ISBN 978-1-60262-326-2

Bridges Grade 1
Home Connections

Unit 1
Numbers All Around Us

Unit 2
Developing Strategies with Dice & Dominoes

Unit 3
Adding, Subtracting, Counting & Comparing

Unit 4
Leapfrogs on the Number Line

Unit 5
Geometry

Unit 6
Figure the Facts with Penguins

Unit 7
One Hundred & Beyond

Unit 8
Changes, Changes

NAME | **DATE**

🏠 Ten Ladybugs page 1 of 2

Look at the pictures of the gray and white ladybugs below. It looks like they are making a number rack! Fill in the correct number in the empty box to make the equation true.

1 $9 +$ ☐ $= 10$

2 $8 +$ ☐ $= 10$

3 $7 +$ ☐ $= 10$

4 $6 +$ ☐ $= 10$

5 $5 +$ ☐ $= 10$

6 $4 +$ ☐ $= 10$

7 $3 +$ ☐ $= 10$

8 $2 +$ ☐ $= 10$

9 $1 +$ ☐ $= 10$

(continued on next page)

🏠 1

Ten Ladybugs page 2 of 2

Look at this number rack. It has one row of 10 beads. How many beads are under the cover?

10

11

12

13

14

15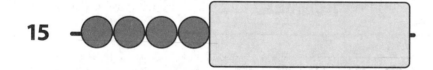

16

17

18

19

2

Changes, Changes page 1 of 2

Fill in the missing number.

1   I started with…   I finished with…   How many did I add?

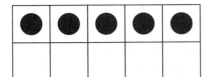

2   I started with…   I finished with…   How many did I add?

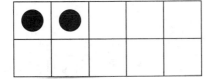

3   I started with…   I finished with…   How many did I take away?

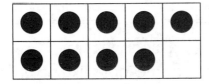

4   I started with…   I finished with…   How many did I add?

4 dots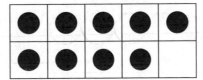

(continued on next page)

NAME | **DATE**

Changes, Changes page 2 of 2

5 I started with… I finished with… How many did I add?

2 dots

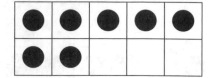

---

6 I started with… I finished with… How many did I take away?

8 dots

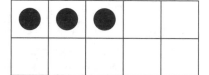

---

7 I started with… I added… How many do I have now?

3 dots **4 more**

---

8 I started with… I added… This is what my ten-frame looks like now.

some dots **3 more**

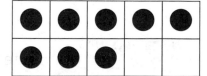

How many dots did I start with? What did my ten-frame look like at the beginning? Fill in the dots.

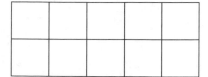

NAME _____ | DATE _____

 Show Me Combinations page 1 of 2

1

I see _____ counters.

I need _____ more to make 10.

2

I see _____ counters.

I need _____ more to make 10.

3

I see _____ counters.

I need _____ more to make 10.

4

I see _____ counters.

I need _____ more to make 10.

(continued on next page)

NAME _____ | DATE _____

Show Me Combinations page 2 of 2

5

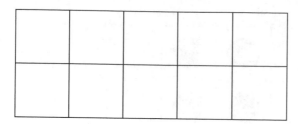

Show me 8 counters.

8 + _____ = 10

6

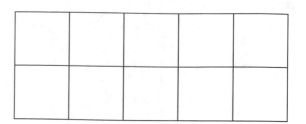

Show me 6 counters.

6 + _____ = 10

7

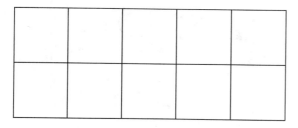

Show me 1 counter.

1 + _____ = 10

8

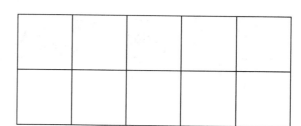

Show me 7 counters.

7 + _____ = 10

6

Popsicle Tallies page 1 of 2

Note to Families

We have been making different kinds of graphs in school. This one uses tally marks to show how many votes each Popsicle flavor got. Help your child read and answer the questions about the graph and then make his or her own graph.

A first grade class voted on their favorite Popsicle flavors. They used tally marks to show how many votes each flavor got.

Flavor	Votes
Cherry	ⵜ⵬ ||||
Orange	ⵜ|||
Grape	ⵜ||

1 How many votes did Cherry get? _____

2 How many votes did Orange get? _____

3 How many votes did Grape get? _____

4 How many votes were there in all? _____

5 Draw a circle around the name of the flavor that got the most votes.

    Cherry   Orange   Grape

6 Draw a line under the name of the flavor that got the least votes.

    Cherry   Orange   Grape

7 Write a statement about the flavor you circled and the flavor you underlined.

_____ > _____

(continued on next page)

NAME _____ | DATE _____

Popsicle Tallies page 2 of 2

Now make your own tally graph, this time making it about the lights in some of the rooms in your home. Count the lights in each room listed and make tally marks to show how many. The lights might be on the ceiling, on the floor, on a table, or under a counter.

Room	How many lights?
Kitchen	
Living Room	
Bedroom	

8 How many lights are in the kitchen? _____

9 How many lights are in the living room? _____

10 How many lights are in the bedroom? _____

11 How many lights in all? _____

12 Draw a circle around the name of the room with the most lights.

Kitchen   Living Room   Bedroom

13 Draw a line under the name of the room with the fewest lights.

Kitchen   Living Room   Bedroom

14 Write a statement about the room you circled and the room you underlined.

_____ > _____

NAME _____ | DATE _____

🏠 One More, One Less page 1 of 2

ex Show 4 on the ten-frame.

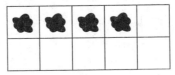

Now show 1 *more.*

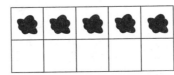

4 + 1 = ____5____

1 Show 3 on the ten-frame.

3 + 1 = _____

Now show 1 *more.*

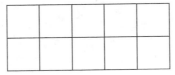

2 Show 7 on the ten-frame.

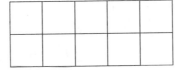

7 + 1 = _____

Now show 1 *more.*

3 Show 5 on the ten-frame.

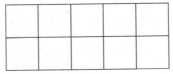

5 + 1 = _____

Now show 1 *more.*

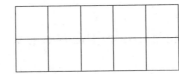

4 Show 6 on the ten-frame.

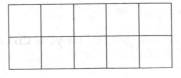

6 + 1 = _____

Now show 1 *more.*

(continued on next page)

NAME _____ | DATE _____

One More, One Less page 2 of 2

5 Show 5 on the ten-frame.

Now show 1 *less*.

$5 - 1 = $ _____

6 Show 10 on the ten-frame.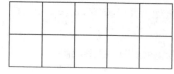

Now show 1 *less*.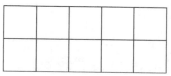

$10 - 1 = $ _____

7 Show 7 on the ten-frame.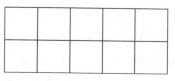

Now show 1 *less*.

$7 - 1 = $ _____

8 What number is 1 more than 9? _____   1 less than 9? _____

9 What number is 1 more than 4? _____   1 less than 4? _____

10 What number is 1 more than 2? _____   1 less than 2? _____

Challenge

11 What number is 1 more than 99? _____   1 less than 99? _____

12 What number is 1 more than 250? _____   1 less than 250? _____

13 What number is 1 more than 301? _____   1 less than 301? _____

14 What number is 1 more than 410? _____   1 less than 410? _____

NAME _____ | DATE _____

 Which Coin Will Win? page 1 of 4

Note to Families

This is an activity that your child has done in school. Have him or her show you how to play, and take turns playing together! (Players do not compete with each other in this activity.) While practicing graphing and identifying coins, students are also thinking about probability—what are the chances of landing on a penny or a nickel with each spinner?

Materials

- Which Coin Will Win? pages 1–4
- 10 pennies and 10 nickels (or any item to represent the coins)
- crayon or pencil
- paperclip and pencil to be used as a spinner

Instructions

1 Locate the spinners on page 2. Play begins with Spinner A.

2 The player uses the paperclip as an arrow for the spinner by holding the pencil point in the middle of the chosen spinner and spinning the paperclip around it. If it points to a nickel, set a nickel on the graph (working from the bottom to the top). If it spins on a penny, set a penny on the graph.

   Note Students should not mark on the game board like they did in school. This way, the game board can be used over and over again.

3 The player keeps spinning until one column is filled to the top.

4 The player colors a space on the graph (under Spinner A on the Which Coin Will Win? record sheet on page 3) to show which coin won the race to the top of the column.

5 Play with Spinner A continues for seven complete rounds (a round is complete when one coin has raced to the top and the player has recorded the results on the appropriate graph).

6 The player switches to Spinner B, and play continues for seven complete rounds.

7 Players think about the results: Did both spinners give each coin a fair chance to win? Why or why not?

8 The student completes page 4 of this assignment and returns pages 3 and 4 to school.

(continued on next page)

12

NAME _____ | DATE _____

Which Coin Will Win? page 2 of 4

Spinner A

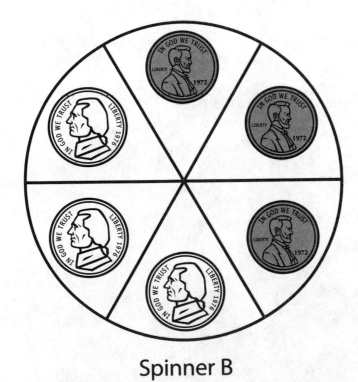

Spinner B

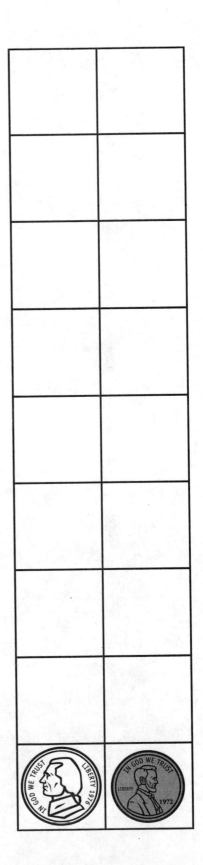

(continued on next page)

14

NAME _____ | DATE _____

Which Coin Will Win? page 3 of 4

Use this record sheet to record the results each time you play Which Coin Will Win? Locate the appropriate spinner and color in a space on the graph above the coin that won. There's enough room to record the results of seven games with each spinner.

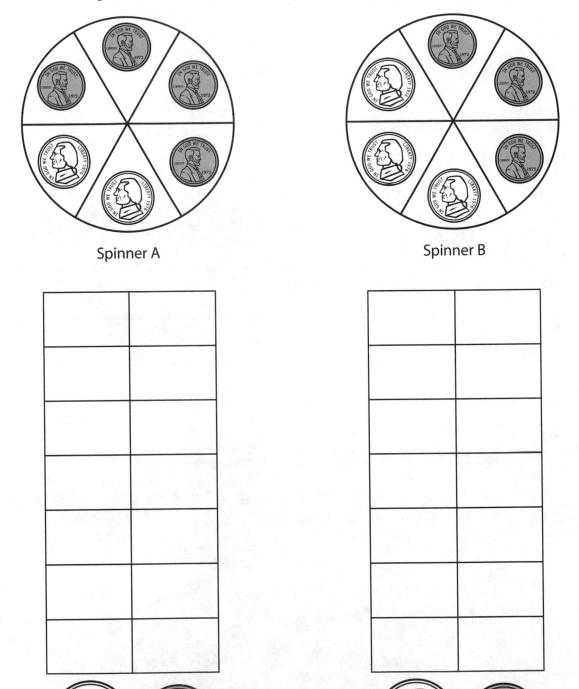

Spinner A   Spinner B

(continued on next page)

NAME | DATE

Which Coin Will Win? page 4 of 4

You have played Which Coin Will Win? many times. Now it's time to look at your record sheet to see how things turned out. Were the results from each spinner the same or different?

1 Spinner A

a How many times did the nickels 🪙 win? _____

b How many times did the pennies 🪙 win? _____

c Write a greater than (>) or less than (<) sign to show whether the nickel had more wins or fewer wins than the penny. 🪙 ☐ 🪙

d Write an equation to show how many times the nickels won, how many times the pennies won, and how many wins in all.

_____ + _____ = _____

2 Spinner B

a How many times did the nickels 🪙 win? _____

b How many times did the pennies 🪙 win? _____

c Write a greater than (>) or less than (<) sign to show whether the nickel had more wins or fewer wins than the penny. 🪙 ☐ 🪙

d Write an equation to show how times the nickels won, how many times the pennies won, and how many wins in all.

_____ + _____ = _____

3 Talk about these questions with someone:

- Did one of the spinners give the pennies a better chance to win?
- If so, which one?
- Why or why not?

🏠 One More Dot, One Less Dot page 1 of 2

1 In the table below:

- Look at the domino in the middle and write how many dots you see.
- In the box to the left, write the number that is 1 less than the number of dots on the domino.
- In the box to the right, write the number that is 1 more than the number of dots on the domino.

One Less Dot	How Many Dots?		One More Dot
ex 6	(domino)	7	8
a	(domino)		
b	(domino)		
c	(domino)		
d	(domino)		
e	(domino)		
f	(domino)		

(continued on next page)

NAME | DATE

One More Dot, One Less Dot page 2 of 2

2 In the table below:

- Look at the number in the middle and draw that many dots on the domino.
- In the box to the left, put an X on the domino with 1 less dot than your domino.
- In the box to the right, put an X on the domino with 1 more dot than your domino.

One Less Dot	Draw the Dots	One More Dot
ex	4	
a	5	
b	8	
c	6	
d	9	

NAME _____ | **DATE** _____

 Domino Magic Squares page 1 of 2

How many dots?

Add the dots on the dominoes going down each column and then going across each row. Then add the sums both ways, vertically and horizontally. Do you get the same total both times? Is it magic, or is there a mathematical explanation?

ex

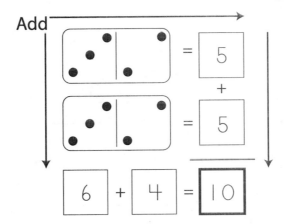

1 Add

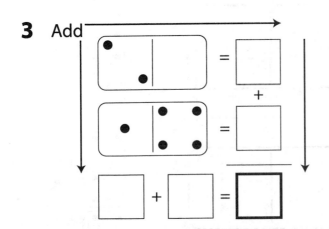

2 Add

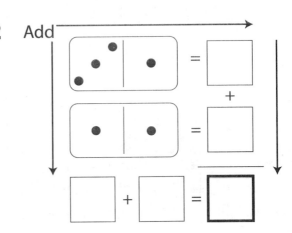

3 Add

4 Add

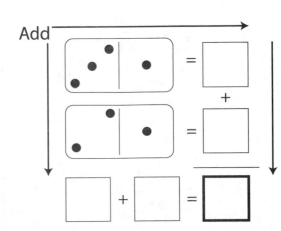

(continued on next page)

Domino Magic Squares page 2 of 2

5 Add
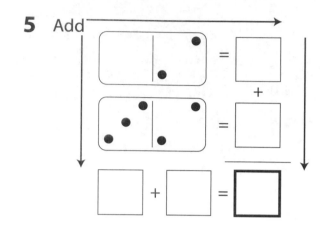

6 Add
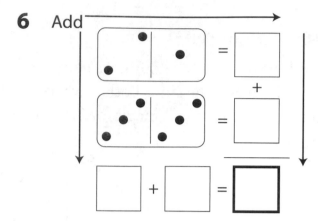

Challenge Problems

7 Add

8 Add

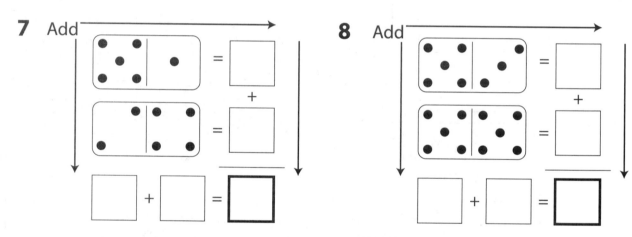

Make up your own magic square problem below. Draw between 1 and 6 dots on each side of the two dominoes. Then add the dots on the dominoes going down and going across. Then add the sums both ways. Do you get the same total both times? Is it magic?

Add
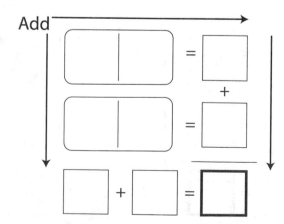

20

More Domino Magic Squares page 1 of 2

How many dots?

Add the dots on the dominoes going down each column and then going across each row. Then add the sums both ways, vertically and horizontally. Do you get the same total both times? Is it magic, or is there a mathematical explanation?

ex

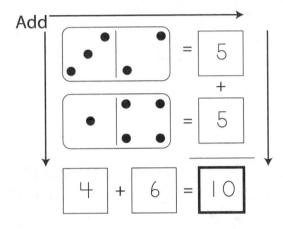

Add →

= 5
+
= 5

4 + 6 = 10

1 Add →

=
+
=

☐ + ☐ = ☐

2 Add →

=
+
=

☐ + ☐ = ☐

3 Add →

=
+
=

☐ + ☐ = ☐

4 Add →

=
+
=

☐ + ☐ = ☐

(continued on next page)

NAME | DATE

More Domino Magic Squares page 2 of 2

5 Add

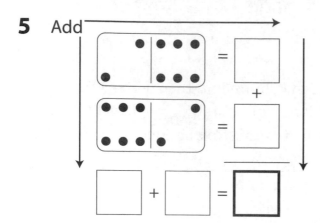

6 Add

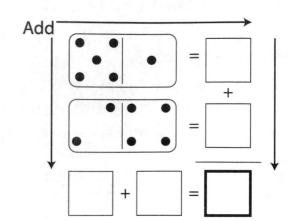

Challenge Problems

7 Add

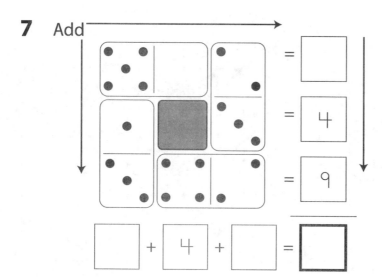

8 Add

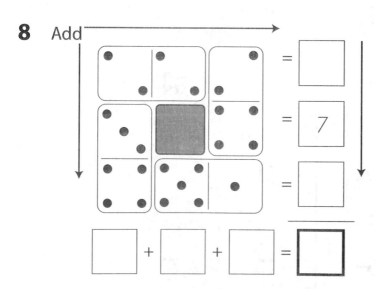

NAME _____ DATE _____

Numbers & Domino Dots page 1 of 2

1 Trace each number.

| 1 | 2 | 3 | 4 | 5 | 6 | 7 | 8 | 9 | 0 |

2 Fill in the missing numbers.

1	2	3		5	6	7		9	10
11	12		14	15		17	18		20
21		23		25	26			29	30
31				35		37			40

(continued on next page)

23

NAME _____ | DATE _____

Numbers & Domino Dots page 2 of 2

Solve the problems about dominoes below.

3 Sam has a domino with 4 dots on it. Draw the dots on this domino to show how Sam's domino looks.

4 Maria's domino has 1 less dot than Tim's. Draw the dots on Tim's domino to show how it looks.

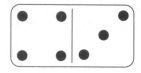

Maria's domino

Tim's domino

How many dots? _____   How many dots? _____

5 Jeff's domino has 6 dots. Draw dots on the dominoes below to show three different dominoes that Jeff might have.

6 **CHALLENGE** Tom has a domino with some dots. Kim's domino has 2 more dots than Tom's. Draw dots on these two dominoes to show how Tom's and Kim's dominoes look.

Tom's domino

Kim's domino

How many dots? _____   How many dots? _____

24

NAME _____ | DATE _____

🏠 Dots, Apples & Shapes page 1 of 2

1 Draw the dots on the right side of each card to make 10.
Then write a fact family to match.

ex

$$6 + 4 = 10$$
$$4 + 6 = 10$$
$$10 - 6 = 4$$
$$10 - 4 = 6$$

a

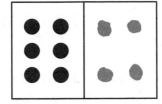 _____
_____
_____
_____

b

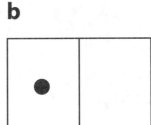 _____
_____
_____
_____

c

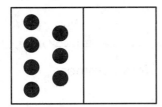 _____
_____
_____
_____

d

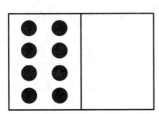 _____
_____
_____
_____

2 Fill in the missing numbers.

$9 + \boxed{} = 10$ $\boxed{} + 1 = 10$ $4 + 6 = \boxed{}$ $10 + \boxed{} = 10$

$10 - 6 = \boxed{}$ $10 - 7 = \boxed{}$ $10 - 1 = \boxed{}$ $10 - 8 = \boxed{}$

$10 - \boxed{} = 6$ $\boxed{} - 1 = 9$ $10 - 4 = \boxed{}$ $10 - \boxed{} = 8$

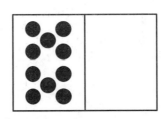

(continued on next page)

25

Dots, Apples & Shapes page 2 of 2

3 There were 3 apples on the table. Jan put 6 more apples on the table. How many apples were on the table in all? Show your work.

There were _____ apples on the table in all.

4 **CHALLENGE** Make a picture that is worth 14¢. You can use as many as you like of these shapes. Label your picture. Prove that it is worth 14¢.

Square: 5¢

Circle: 2¢

Triangle: 1¢

NAME _____ | DATE _____

Dots & Dollars page 1 of 2

1 Draw the dots on the right side of each card to make 9.
Then write a fact family to match.

ex

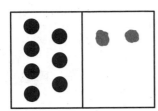

7 + 2 = 9
2 + 7 = 9
9 – 7 = 2
9 – 2 = 7

a

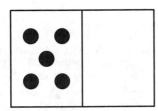

_____
_____
_____

b

_____
_____
_____

c

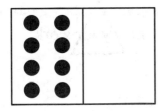

_____
_____
_____

d

_____
_____
_____

2 Fill in the missing numbers.

9 + ☐ = 9   ☐ + 7 = 9   6 + 3 = ☐   9 + ☐ = 9

9 – 3 = ☐   9 – 6 = ☐   9 – 4 = ☐   9 – 5 = ☐

9 – ☐ = 0   ☐ – 2 = 7   9 – 8 = ☐   9 – ☐ = 5

(continued on next page)

NAME | DATE

Dots & Dollars page 2 of 2

3 Marco has 6 dollars. How many more dollars does he need to have 10 dollars in all? Show your work.

Marco needs _____ dollars to have 10 dollars in all.

4 **CHALLENGE** Katy and her two friends have 5 dollars each. They want to buy a game that costs 18 dollars. How much more money do they need? Show your work.

Katy and her friends need _____ more dollars to have 18 dollars in all.

Addition & Subtraction Practice page 1 of 2

1 Trace the word and write it again 4 times.

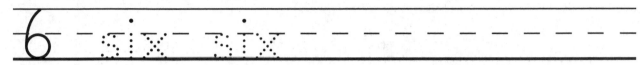

2 Fill in the answers for each of the problems.

a Add.

3 + 3 = _____   2 + 4 = _____   1 + 5 = _____

0 + 6 = _____   4 + 2 = _____   5 + 1 = _____

3 + _____ = 6   5 + _____ = 6   4 + _____ = 6

b Subtract.

6 – 3 = _____   6 – 4 = _____   6 – 0 = _____

6 – 2 = _____   6 – 5 = _____   6 – 1 = _____

6 – _____ = 3   6 – _____ = 1   6 – _____ = 4

3 CHALLENGE Fill in the missing numbers in the equations below.

30 + 30 = _____   20 + 40 = _____   50 + _____ = 60

10 + _____ = 60   30 + _____ = 60   40 + _____ = 60

20 + _____ + 20 = 60   40 + _____ +10 = 60   40 + 0 + _____ = 60

30 + 10 + _____ = 60   10 + 20 + _____ = 60   50 + 10 + _____ = 60

(continued on next page)

NAME _____ | DATE _____

Addition & Subtraction Practice page 2 of 2

4 Fill in the blanks.

6 – _____ = 1   6 – _____ = 2   6 – _____ = 4

6 – _____ = 0   6 – _____ = 6   6 – _____ = 5

_____ – 4 = 2   _____ – 3 = 3   6 – 1 = _____

6 – 4 = _____   6 – 2 = _____   6 – 5 = _____

5 Solve the subtraction problems.

$$\begin{array}{ccccccc} 5 & 4 & 1 & 3 & 5 & 2 & 3 \\ -2 & -2 & -1 & -0 & -1 & -2 & -2 \end{array}$$

$$\begin{array}{ccccccc} 5 & 4 & 3 & 3 & 5 & 4 & 2 \\ -3 & -1 & -3 & -1 & -0 & -0 & -1 \end{array}$$

$$\begin{array}{ccccccc} 1 & 4 & 5 & 2 & 5 & 4 & 0 \\ -0 & -3 & -4 & -0 & -5 & -4 & -0 \end{array}$$

7 There were 6 bugs outside the house. Some of them went inside to get warm. Now there are only 2 bugs outside the house. How many bugs went inside? Use numbers, pictures, or words to solve this problem.

_____ bugs went inside the house.

NAME _____ | **DATE** _____

🏠 Counting by Fives & Tens page 1 of 2

1 For each row, count how many arms the sea stars have, and write that number in the box on the right side.

one		arms
two		arms
three		arms
four		arms
five		arms

2 Continue the counting by 5s pattern.

0	0
0	5
1	0
1	5

3 Max saw 7 sea stars. How many arms? Use numbers, pictures, or words to solve the problem.

Max saw _____ sea star arms.

(continued on next page)

31

NAME

DATE

Counting by Fives & Tens page 2 of 2

4 Count the cubes in each box. Write the number on the line.

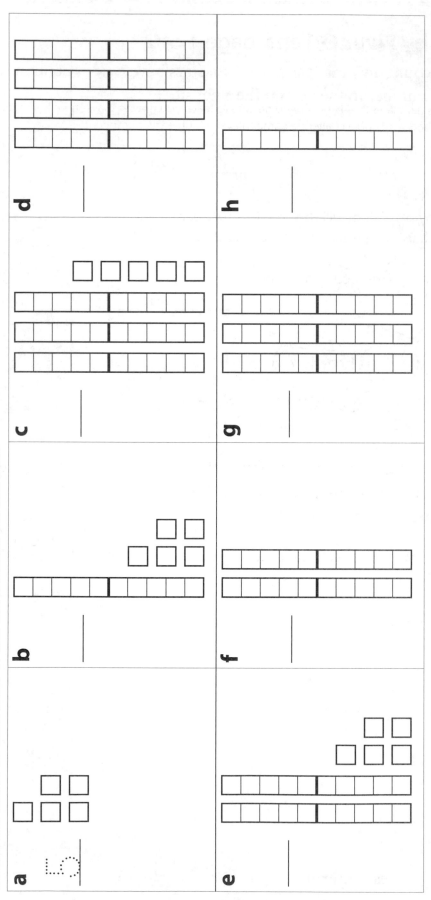

a _____

b _____

c _____

d _____

e _____

f _____

g _____

h _____

5 Fill in the missing numbers on the number line. You can use the cubes above to help you count.

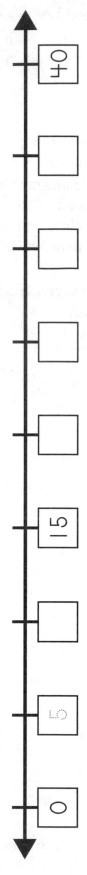

0 ___ 5 ___ 15 ___ ___ ___ 40

Double It page 1 of 3

Note to Families

Your child has played this game in school and should be able to teach you how to play! There is a regular game (players double the numbers 1–6) and a challenge game (players double the numbers 1–10).

Materials

- Double It pages 1–3
- game markers—any small item will do: pennies, dry beans, Legos, and so on (6 of each for the regular game; 10 of each for the challenge game)
- pencil and a paperclip to be used as a spinner arrow

Instructions

1 Choose one of the game boards and collect your game markers.

2 Use the paperclip as an arrow. While holding the pencil point down in the middle of the spinner, spin the paperclip around it.

3 Take turns spinning the spinner, doubling the number, and covering the sum on your side of the game board. (For example: If you spin 3, double it to 6, and cover the 6 on the game board.)

4 If you spin a number that you have already covered, you will have to wait until your next turn to try again.

5 The first person to cover all six of their numbers is the winner!

6 **CHALLENGE** For the Double It Challenge game, you need to spin the 0–5 spinner twice, add the numbers, and then double the sum. (For example, if you spin 3 and 5, you add them to get 8 and then double 8 to get 16. Cover the number 16 on your game board.)

34

NAME _____

DATE _____

Double It page 2 of 3

| 2 |
| 4 |
| 6 |
| 8 |
| 10 |
| 12 |

| 12 |
| 10 |
| 8 |
| 6 |
| 4 |
| 2 |

Spinner numbers: 2, 3, 4, 5, 6, 1

Double It

NAME

DATE

Double It page 3 of 3

20	18	16	14	12	10	8	6	4	2

Double It Challenge

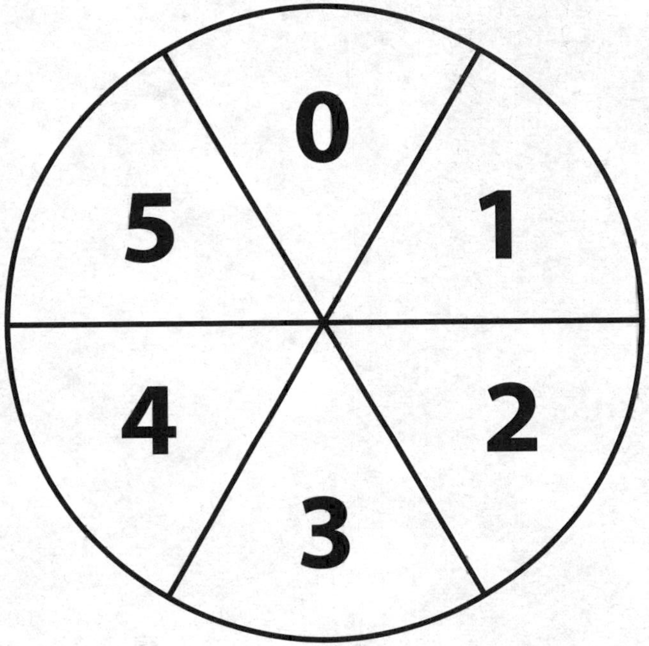

2	4	6	8	10	12	14	16	18	20

38

Counting & Adding Practice page 1 of 2

1 Trace the numerals and the number words.

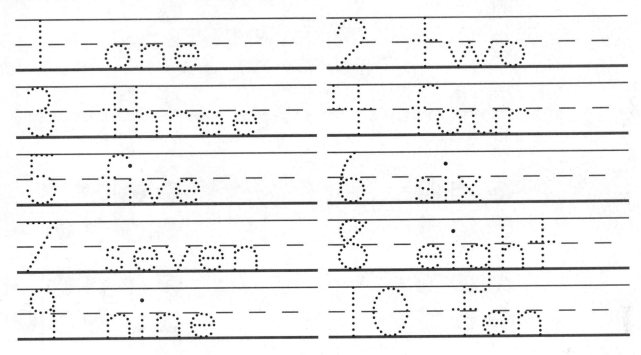

2 How many bugs are in each frame? Write the numeral and the number word.

a

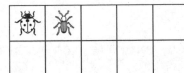

b

c

d

e

f

g

h

i

(continued on next page)

NAME _____ | DATE _____

Counting & Adding Practice page 2 of 2

3 Solve the problems below.

a $\begin{array}{r} 1 \\ + 1 \\ \hline \end{array}$

b $\begin{array}{r} 1 \\ + 2 \\ \hline \end{array}$

c $\begin{array}{r} 2 \\ + 2 \\ \hline \end{array}$

d $\begin{array}{r} 2 \\ + 3 \\ \hline \end{array}$

e $\begin{array}{r} 3 \\ + 3 \\ \hline \end{array}$

f $\begin{array}{r} 3 \\ + 4 \\ \hline \end{array}$

g $\begin{array}{r} 4 \\ + 4 \\ \hline \end{array}$

h $\begin{array}{r} 4 \\ + 5 \\ \hline \end{array}$

i $\begin{array}{r} 5 \\ + 4 \\ \hline \end{array}$

j $\begin{array}{r} 5 \\ + 5 \\ \hline \end{array}$

4 Fill in the blank to complete each equation.

$3 + 4 =$ _____ $4 + 5 =$ _____ $2 + 3 =$ _____ $5 + 6 =$ _____

$4 +$ _____ $= 8$ $2 +$ _____ $= 4$ $3 +$ _____ $= 6$ $5 +$ _____ $= 10$

$10 - 5 =$ _____ $6 - 3 =$ _____ $8 - 4 =$ _____ $4 - 2 =$ _____

5 CHALLENGE Fill in the blank to complete each equation.

$40 + 30 =$ _____ $50 + 40 =$ _____ $50 + 60 =$ _____ $30 + 20 =$ _____

40

NAME _____ | DATE _____

 Sixes, Crayons & Coins page 1 of 2

1 Write an equation to match each cube train.

ex
$$3 + 3 = 6$$

a

b

c

2 Color in the train to match each equation.

ex $4 + 2 = 6$

a $3 + 2 + 1 = 6$
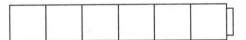

b $1 + 5 = 6$

c $1 + 4 + 1 = 6$

3 Subtract.

$6 - 0 =$ _____ $5 - 2 =$ _____ $5 - 5 =$ _____ $6 - 2 =$ _____

$6 - 4 =$ _____ $6 - 1 =$ _____ $6 - 3 =$ _____ $5 - 4 =$ _____

$6 - 5 =$ _____ $5 - 3 =$ _____ $6 - 6 =$ _____ $5 - 1 =$ _____

4 Fill in the missing number.

$2 +$ _____ $= 6$ _____ $+ 5 = 6$ $6 = 3 +$ _____ $6 = 4 +$ _____

$3 +$ _____ $= 6$ _____ $+ 0 = 6$ $6 = 2 +$ _____ $6 = 6 +$ _____

(continued on next page)

Sixes, Crayons & Coins page 2 of 2

5 John had some crayons. He gave 5 to Jen. Now he has 7 crayons left. How many crayons did John have to start with? Show your work.

John started out with _____ crayons.

6 **CHALLENGE** Here are three clues:

- Kendra has 5 coins.
- She has 35¢.
- She has only nickels and dimes.

How many nickels does Kendra have? How many dimes does Kendra have? Show your work.

Kendra has _____ nickels. Kendra has _____ dimes.

42

🏠 Ten & Twenty page 1 of 2

How many more to make 10?

1 How many more beads do you need to make 10 in all? Write the number in the box at the right of each bead string.

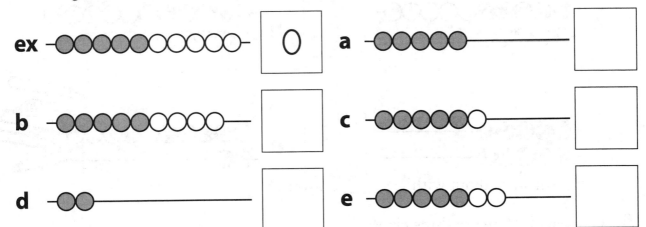

2 Fill in the box to complete each equation.

$6 + \boxed{} = 10$ $4 + \boxed{} = 10$ $7 + \boxed{} = 10$ $3 + \boxed{} = 10$

$10 = 8 + \boxed{}$ $10 = 2 + \boxed{}$ $10 = 5 + \boxed{}$ $10 = 9 + \boxed{}$

3 Are these equations correct? Circle *yes* or *no* to show.

$5 + 4 = 10$	Yes	No	$5 + 5 = 10$	Yes	No
$10 = 1 + 9$	Yes	No	$10 = 7 + 2$	Yes	No
$2 + 3 + 5 = 10$	Yes	No	$1 + 2 + 3 + 4 = 10$	Yes	No

(continued on next page)

43

NAME _____ | **DATE** _____

Ten & Twenty page 2 of 2

How Many More to Make 20?

4 How many more beads do you need to make 20 in all? Write the number in the box at the right of each pair of bead strings.

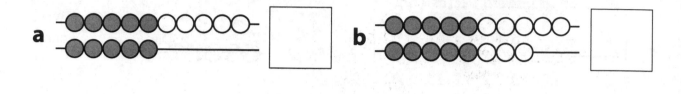

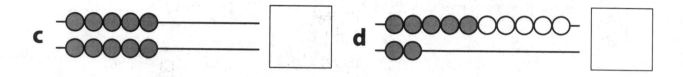

5 Dan had 10 mini racer cars. He got 6 more mini racer cars for his birthday. Then his brother gave him 4 more mini racer cars.

a How many mini racer cars does Dan have in all? Show your work.

b Dan has _____ mini racer cars in all.

Tens & Ones page 1 of 2

1 Circle the counting-by-10s numbers in the grid below. Use this grid to help you figure out the value of each group of coins below:

1	2	3	4	5	6	7	8	9	10
11	12	13	14	15	16	17	18	19	20
21	22	23	24	25	26	27	28	29	30
31	32	33	34	35	36	37	38	39	40
41	42	43	44	45	46	47	48	49	50

Dime
10 cents
10¢

Penny
1 cent
1¢

2 Write the total amount of money for each set:

a _____ ¢

b _____ ¢

c _____ ¢

d _____ ¢

e _____ ¢

(continued on next page)

NAME | **DATE**

Tens & Ones page 2 of 2

1 Trace the numerals and number words. Find the sum in each box. Draw lines to show the matches. You won't find a match for every number word.

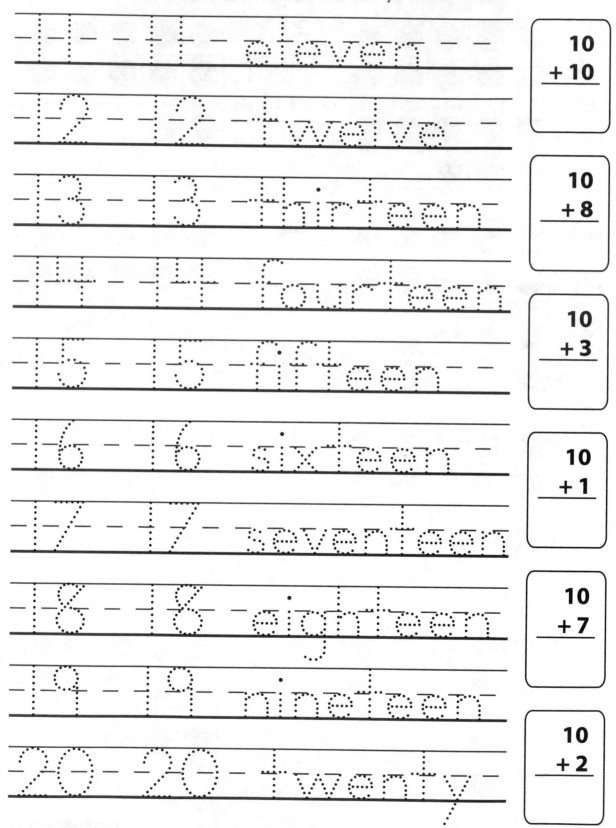

11 11 eleven

12 12 twelve

13 13 thirteen

14 14 fourteen

15 15 fifteen

16 16 sixteen

17 17 seventeen

18 18 eighteen

19 19 nineteen

20 20 twenty

10
+ 10

10
+ 8

10
+ 3

10
+ 1

10
+ 7

10
+ 2

NAME | DATE

 Add Ten Facts page 1 of 2

Fill in each answer below.

1

10
+ 8

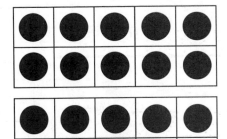

2

10
+ 2

3

10
+ 6

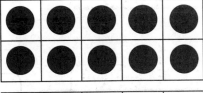

4

10
+ 4

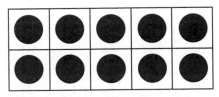

5

10
+ 1

6

10
+ 5

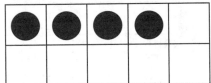

7

10
+ 7

8

10
+ 3

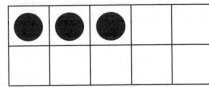

(continued on next page)

NAME _____ | DATE _____

Add Ten Facts page 2 of 2

9 Write the answer to each problem.

10 + 2 = _____   10 + 5 = _____   10 + 9 = _____

10 + 0 = _____   10 + 7 = _____   10 + 4 = _____

10 + 8 = _____   10 + 1 = _____   10 + 3 = _____

10 + 6 = _____   3 + 10 = _____   7 + 10 = _____

8 + 10 = _____   5 + 10 = _____   0 + 10 = _____

1 + 10 = _____   9 + 10 = _____   6 + 10 = _____

4 + 10 = _____   2 + 10 = _____   10 + 10 = _____

10 Fill in the missing numbers.

a Count by 1s

16, _____, _____, 19, _____, _____, 22, _____, 24, _____, _____, _____, 28,

_____, _____, _____

b Count by 10s

10, 20, _____, 40, _____, _____, _____, 80, _____, 100

c Count by 5s

5, 10, 15, _____, _____, 30, _____, 40, _____, _____, 55, _____, _____, 70

d Count backward by 1s

14, 13, _____, 11, _____, 9, 8, _____, _____, 5, _____, _____, _____, 1

11 Fill in the missing numbers.

a Count by _____s.

b 3, 5, _____, 9, 11, _____, _____, 17, _____, _____, 23, _____, 27, _____, 31

Unifix Cube Equations, Sevens page 1 of 2

1 Color in the Unifix cubes in different ways to make 7, and write an equation to match each train.

a

= 7

b

7 =

c

= 7

d

7 =

2 Circle T for true or F for false.

a $3 + 4 = 7$ T   or   F   **b** $7 = 2 + 3 + 1$ T   or   F

c $7 = 3 + 4$ T   or   F   **d** $7 + 0 = 7$ T   or   F

3 Add.

$$\begin{array}{cccccc} 3 & 3 & 2 & 4 & 7 & 2 \\ +4 & +3 & +5 & +2 & +0 & +3 \end{array}$$

$$\begin{array}{cccccc} 2 & 4 & 4 & 6 & 6 & 5 \\ +2 & +3 & +1 & +1 & +0 & +2 \end{array}$$

$3 + 4 = $ _____ $2 + 2 + 2 = $ _____ $5 + 2 = $ _____

(continued on next page)

Unifix Cube Equations, Sevens page 2 of 2

4   Subtract.

7	7	6	7	6	7
− 7	− 0	− 4	− 1	− 3	− 5

7	5	7	5	7	7
− 2	− 2	− 4	− 3	− 3	− 6

7 − 2 = _____   6 − 4 = _____   7 − 4 = _____

5   3 + 4 is one way to make 7. Show four other ways to make 7. You can use addition or subtraction equations.

🏠 Unifix Cube Equations, Eights page 1 of 2

1 Color in the Unifix cubes in different ways to make 8, and write an equation to match each train.

a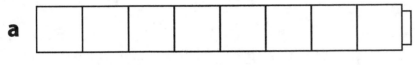

= 8

b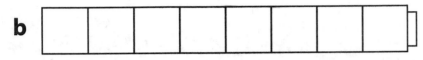

8 =

c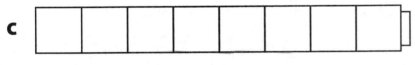

= 8

d

8 =

2 Circle T for true or F for false.

a 5 + 1 = 8   T or F   **b** 8 = 2 + 3 + 1   T or F

c 8 = 4 + 4   T or F   **d** 3 + 5 = 8   T or F

3 Add.

4	4	3	1	8	3
+ 4	+ 3	+ 5	+ 2	+ 0	+ 3

3	5	7	6	2	2
+ 2	+ 3	+ 1	+ 2	+ 5	+ 6

4 + 3 = _____   5 + 3 = _____   4 + 2 + 2 = _____

(continued on next page)

NAME _____ | DATE _____

Unifix Cube Equations, Eights page 2 of 2

4 Subtract.

| $\begin{array}{r} 7 \\ -5 \\ \hline \end{array}$ | $\begin{array}{r} 8 \\ -0 \\ \hline \end{array}$ | $\begin{array}{r} 8 \\ -4 \\ \hline \end{array}$ | $\begin{array}{r} 8 \\ -1 \\ \hline \end{array}$ | $\begin{array}{r} 7 \\ -3 \\ \hline \end{array}$ | $\begin{array}{r} 8 \\ -5 \\ \hline \end{array}$ |

| $\begin{array}{r} 8 \\ -2 \\ \hline \end{array}$ | $\begin{array}{r} 7 \\ -2 \\ \hline \end{array}$ | $\begin{array}{r} 8 \\ -8 \\ \hline \end{array}$ | $\begin{array}{r} 8 \\ -7 \\ \hline \end{array}$ | $\begin{array}{r} 8 \\ -3 \\ \hline \end{array}$ | $\begin{array}{r} 8 \\ -6 \\ \hline \end{array}$ |

$8 - 5 =$ _____ $7 - 5 =$ _____ $8 - 4 =$ _____

5 4 + 4 is one way to make 8. Show four other ways to make 8. You can use addition or subtraction equations.

Doubles & Doubles Plus or Minus One page 1 of 2

1 Color the ten-strips to match each addition problem. Solve each equation.

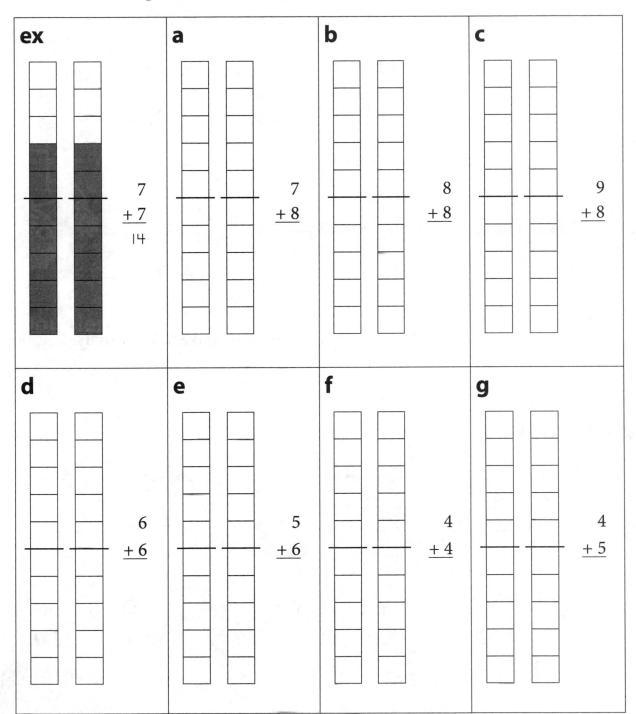

(continued on next page)

Doubles & Doubles Plus or Minus One page 2 of 2

2 Doubles: Solve each problem.

3 + 3 = _____   5 + 5 = _____   2 + 2 = _____

4 + 4 = _____   1 + 1 = _____   0 + 0 = _____

6 + 6 = _____   9 + 9 = _____   8 + 8 = _____

7 + 7 = _____   10 + 10 = _____   4 + 4 = _____

3 Doubles Plus or Minus One: Solve each problem.

3 + 4 = _____   5 + 6 = _____   2 + 3 = _____

4 + 5 = _____   1 + 2 = _____   0 + 1 = _____

6 + 7 = _____   7 + 8 = _____   8 + 9 = _____

4 **CHALLENGE** Solve each problem.

25 + 25 = _____   25 + 26 = _____   26 + 26 = _____

26 + 27 = _____   27 + 27 = _____   27 + 28 = _____

40	20	50	30	60	70	100
+ 40	+ 20	+ 50	+ 30	+ 60	+ 70	+ 100

30	20	40	50	60	200	400
+ 20	+ 30	+ 50	+ 60	+ 70	+ 300	+ 500

NAME _____ | **DATE** _____

 Practice on the Line page 1 of 2

1 Solve each problem. Show your work on the number lines.

a 5 + 3 = _____

b 6 + 4 = _____

c 7 + 2 = _____

d 5 + 5 = _____

2 Write an equation to match each number line.

a
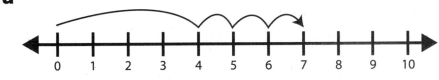

b
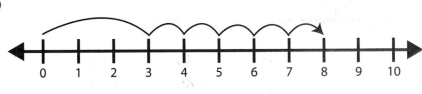

3 Add.

2	4	5	3	6	7	9
+ 2	+ 2	+ 2	+ 5	+ 3	+ 3	+ 0

(continued on next page)

55

NAME _____ | **DATE** _____

Practice on the Line page 2 of 2

4 Solve each problem. Show your work on the number lines.

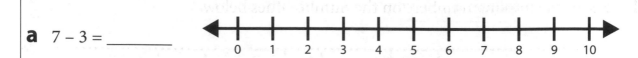

a 7 – 3 = _____

b 9 – 5 = _____

c 6 – 4 = _____

d 8 – 3 = _____

5 Write an equation to match each number line.

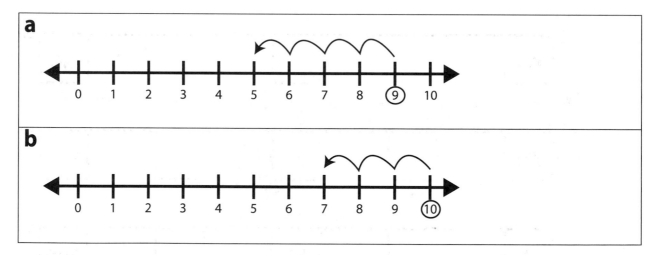

a

b

6 Subtract.

6	4	5	3	7	8	2
– 2	– 1	– 3	– 2	– 5	– 4	– 2

Fives & Tens on the Line page 1 of 2

1 Fill in the missing numbers on the number lines below.

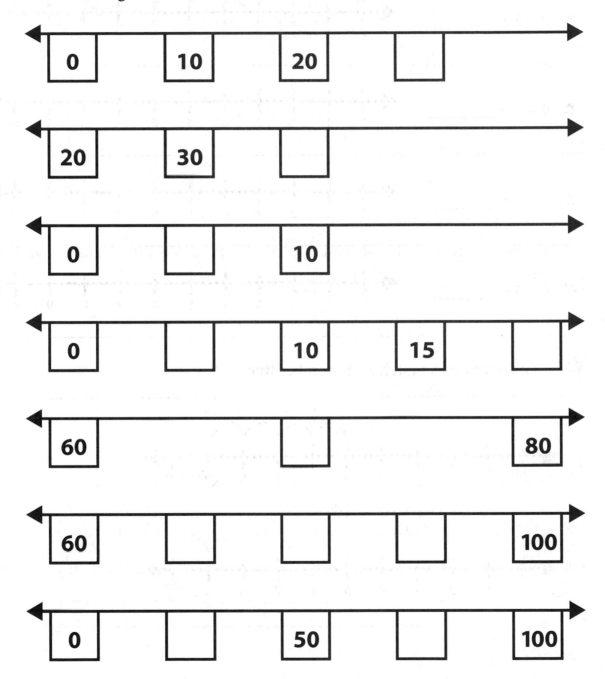

2 Fill in the blanks to answer the questions.

a What comes after 30 if you count by 10s?

20	30	

(continued on next page)

NAME | DATE

Fives & Tens on the Line page 2 of 2

b What number is 10 less than 40?

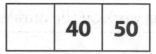

	40	50

c When you count by 10s, what comes before 20? What comes after 50?

	20	30	40	50	

d What comes after 90 when you count by 10s?

70	80	90	

e When you count by 10s, what number comes before 110? What number comes after 110?

70	80	90		110	

f What numbers come after 10, 20, and 30 when you count by 5s?

5	10		20		30		

g What numbers come after 90, 100, and 120 when you count by 5s?

85	90		100		110	115	120	

3 **CHALLENGE** Fill in the missing number on the number line below. Explain your answer.

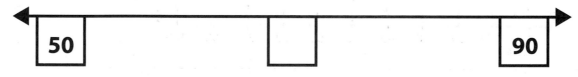

50			90

a Here is why I wrote _____ in the empty box:

🏠 Practice on the Line to One Hundred page 1 of 2

1 Solve each problem. Show your work on the number lines.

a 50 + 30 = _____

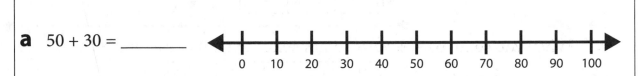

b 60 + 40 = _____

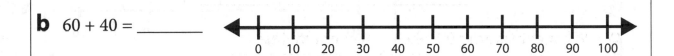

c 70 + 20 = _____

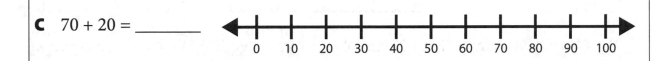

d 50 + 50 = _____

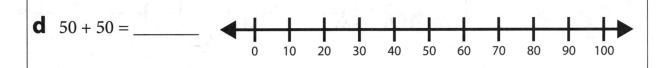

2 Write an equation to match each number line.

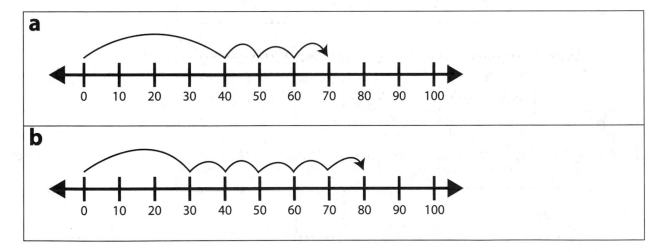

a

b

3 Add.

20	40	50	30	60	70	90
+ 20	+ 20	+ 20	+ 50	+ 30	+ 30	+ 0

(continued on next page)

59

NAME _____ | DATE _____

Practice on the Line to One Hundred page 2 of 2

4 Solve each problem. Show your work on the number lines.

a 70 – 30 = _____
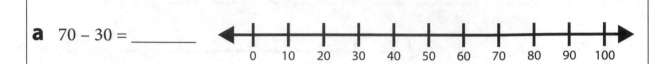

b 90 – 50 = _____

c 60 – 40 = _____
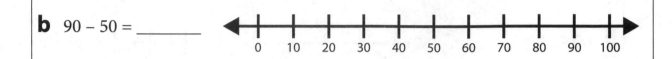

d 80 – 30 = _____
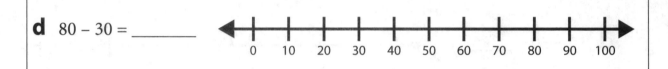

5 Write an equation to match each number line.

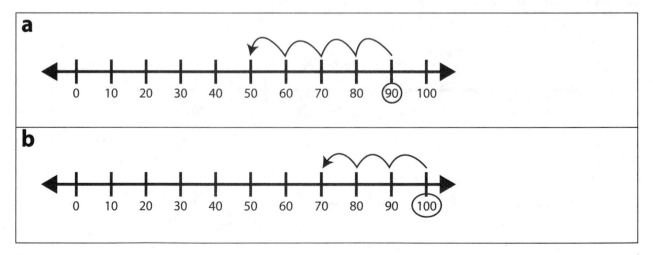

a

b

6 Subtract.

60	40	50	30	70	80	20
– 20	– 10	– 30	– 20	– 50	– 40	– 20

60

NAME | DATE

 Hungry Shark Subtraction page 1 of 2

1 Solve each problem.

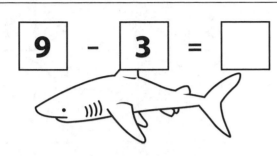

9 – 3 =

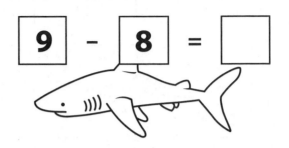

9 – 8 =

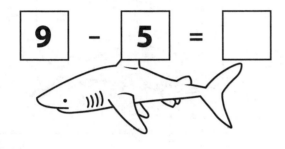

9 – 5 =

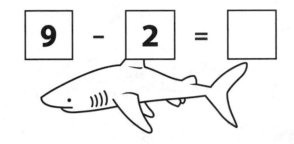

9 – 2 =

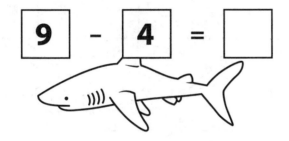

9 – 4 =

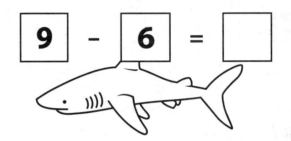

9 – 6 =

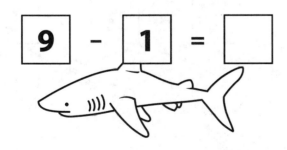

9 – 1 =

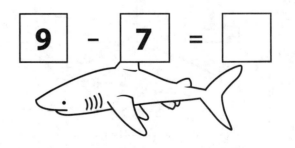

9 – 7 =

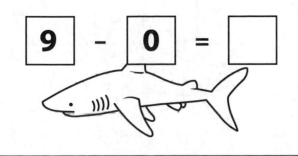

9 – 0 =

9 – 9 =

(continued on next page)

NAME | DATE

Hungry Shark Subtraction page 2 of 2

2 Fill in the empty box for each problem.

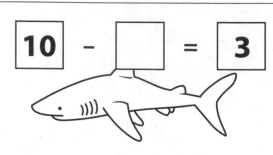 10 – ☐ = 3

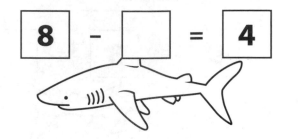 8 – ☐ = 4

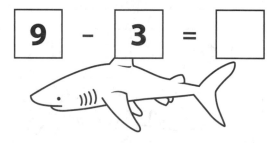 9 – 3 = ☐

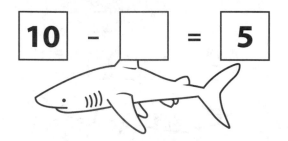 10 – ☐ = 5

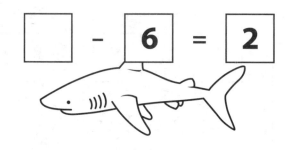 ☐ – 6 = 2

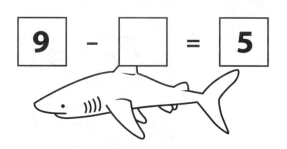 9 – ☐ = 5

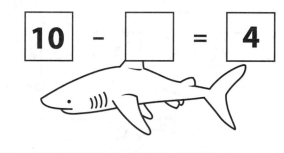 10 – ☐ = 4

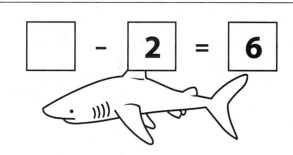 ☐ – 2 = 6

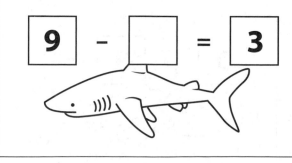 9 – ☐ = 3

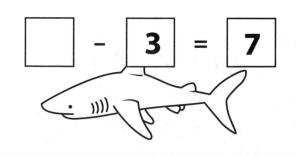 ☐ – 3 = 7

62

NAME _____ | DATE _____

🏠 Sevens, Pennies, Bikes & Trikes page 1 of 2

1 Write an equation to match each cube train.

ex
$$5 + 2 = 7$$

a
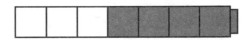

b
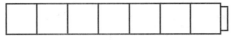

c
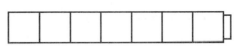

2 Color in the cube train to match the equation.

ex
$$2 + 2 + 3 = 7$$

a
$$2 + 5 = 7$$

b
$$1 + 3 + 3 = 7$$
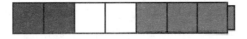

c
$$7 + 0 = 7$$

3 Subtract.

$7 - 0 =$ _____ $6 - 2 =$ _____ $7 - 6 =$ _____ $7 - 2 =$ _____

$7 - 4 =$ _____ $7 - 1 =$ _____ $7 - 3 =$ _____ $6 - 4 =$ _____

$7 - 5 =$ _____ $6 - 3 =$ _____ $7 - 7 =$ _____ $6 - 1 =$ _____

4 Fill in the missing numbers.

$3 +$ _____ $= 7$ _____ $+ 5 = 7$ $7 = 6 +$ _____ $7 = 4 +$ _____

(continued on next page)

Sevens, Pennies, Bikes & Trikes page 2 of 2

5 Tammy has 14 pennies. Troy has 5 pennies. How many more pennies does Tammy have than Troy?

Tammy has _____ more pennies than Troy.

6 **CHALLENGE** Some bikes and trikes are on the playground. There are 7 seats and 19 wheels. How many bikes are there? How many trikes are there? Show your work.

There are _____ bikes on the playground.

There are _____ trikes on the playground.

NAME _____ | **DATE** _____

 Penguin Problems page 1 of 2

1 Find the difference for each problem below.

2 Fill in the missing number.

_____ – 7 = 3	10 – _____ = 6	10 – _____ = 2
_____ – 4 = 6	10 – _____ = 1	10 – _____ = 5
_____ – 8 = 2	10 – _____ = 0	10 – _____ = 10
10 – _____ = 3	10 – _____ = 4	10 – _____ = 7

(continued on next page)

65

NAME | DATE

Penguin Problems page 2 of 2

3 Use pictures, numbers, and words to show how you solve each problem.

a There are 8 penguins ꔛ on the rocks.
There are 5 penguins in the water. ꔛ
How many more penguins are there on the rocks than in the water?

There are _____ more penguins on the rocks than in the water.

b CHALLENGE There are 14 penguins on the rocks. ꔛ
Half as many are swimming. ꔛ
How many are in the water? How many in all?

There are _____ penguins in the water.

There are _____ penguins in all.

NAME _____ | DATE _____

 Using Tens to Count, Add & Subtract page 1 of 2

Each square represents 1 inch.

1 Figure out how many inches tall each penguin is. Write the number of inches on the line beside each penguin's name.

2 How much taller is the emperor penguin than the gentoo penguin? Show how you figured it out.

3 **CHALLENGE** How much taller are you than the gentoo penguin? Show how you figured it out.

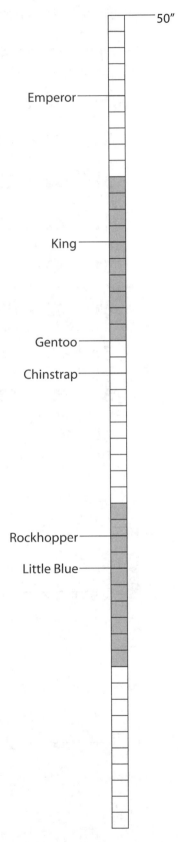

(continued on next page)

67

NAME _____ | DATE _____

Using Tens to Count, Add & Subtract page 2 of 2

Use the Hundreds Grid to help you find the sums and differences below:

1	2	3	4	5	6	7	8	9	10
11	12	13	14	15	16	17	18	19	20
21	22	23	24	25	26	27	28	29	30
31	32	33	34	35	36	37	38	39	40
41	42	43	44	45	46	47	48	49	50
51	52	53	54	55	56	57	58	59	60
61	62	63	64	65	66	67	68	69	70
71	72	73	74	75	76	77	78	79	80
81	82	83	84	85	86	87	88	89	90
91	92	93	94	95	96	97	98	99	100

4 Add.

$63 + 10 =$ _____ $17 + 10 =$ _____ $36 + 10 =$ _____

$10 + 25 =$ _____ $74 + 10 =$ _____ $10 + 38 =$ _____

5 Subtract.

$41 - 10 =$ _____ $85 - 10 =$ _____ $25 - 10 =$ _____

$97 - 10 =$ _____ $52 - 10 =$ _____ $31 - 10 =$ _____

68

NAME _____ | DATE _____

 Fact Families & Shape Patterns page 1 of 2

Draw a line to match each Unifix cube train to its fact family triangle. Then write two addition and two subtraction equations to match.

ex

$3 + 5 = 8$ $8 - 5 = 3$

$5 + 3 = 8$ $8 - 3 = 5$

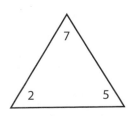

1

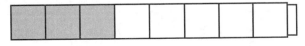

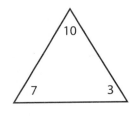

2

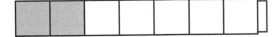

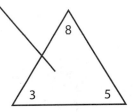

3

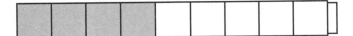

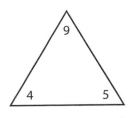

4

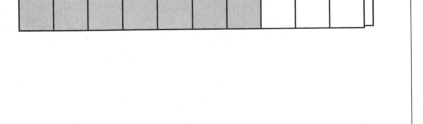

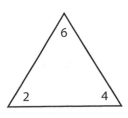

(continued on next page)

NAME | **DATE**

Fact Families & Shape Patterns page 2 of 2

5 Draw the shape and write the number in each empty space on the calendar below. Will the number go on top or on the bottom?

Sunday	Monday	Tuesday	Wednesday	Thursday	Friday	Saturday
			△ 1	◯ 2	▭ 3	◯ 4
▢ 5	△ 6	◯ 7	▭ 8	◯ 9	▢ 10	△ 11
◯ 12	▭ 13	◯ 14	▢ 15	△ 16		
◯ 19	▢ 20	△ 21			◯ 24	
△ 26	◯ 27	▭ 28			△ 31	

6 Draw the shape that is on the second Sunday.

7 Draw the shape that is on the fourth Friday.

8 Draw the shape that is on the first Monday.

NAME

| DATE

 Last Shape In Wins page 1 of 2

Note to Families

Last Shape In Wins is an easy and fun strategy game that gives children a chance to see the results of combining some familiar shapes. We play it at school with pattern blocks, but you'll be coloring in the shapes instead. Have fun!

Materials

- Last Shape In Wins, pages 1 & 2
- crayons, colored pencils, or markers in yellow, green, blue, and red

Instructions

1 With your partner, decide who will go first and who will go second.

2 Take turns coloring in shapes on the first game board.

a You may color in one or more triangles to form one of the shapes shown below.

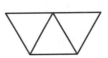
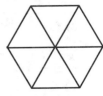

a triangle (color it green)   a rhombus (color it blue)   a trapezoid (color it red)   a hexagon (color it yellow)

b You can color in any one of the four shapes anywhere on the game board each time it's your turn. It is a good idea to outline the shape first before you start coloring.

c You must take your turn every time.

3 The winner is the player who gets to complete filling in the game board (the big rhombus) by coloring in the last shape.

4 **CHALLENGE** Try to use the fewest number of shapes to fill in the big rhombus. See if you can use even fewer the second time you play.

5 When you have time, play the game a second time.

(continued on next page)

Last Shape In Wins page 2 of 2

Game 1

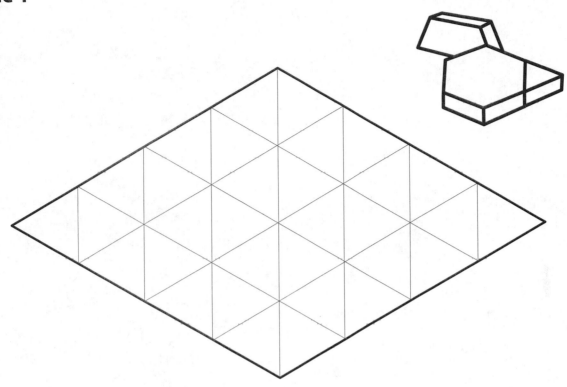

Game 2

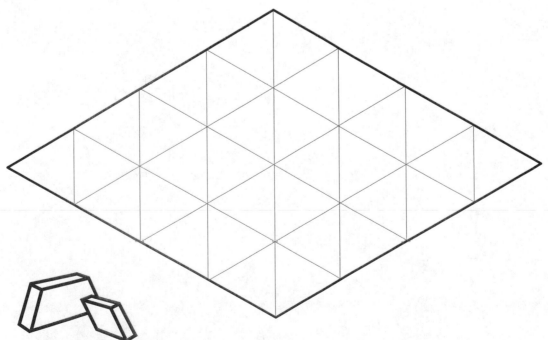

NAME _____ | DATE _____

 ## 3-D Shape Hunt page 1 of 2

You're going to go on a 3-D shape hunt around your house! All you have to do is search for things that are shaped like cubes, spheres, cylinders, and rectangular prisms (boxes), and use drawings or words in each box to show and tell what you found. Happy hunting!

1 Here are some things I found that are cylindrical (shaped like cylinders).

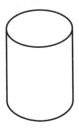

2 Here are some things I found that are shaped like rectangular prisms.

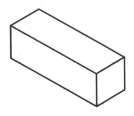

3 Here are some things I found that are spherical (shaped like spheres).

4 Here are some things I found that are shaped like cubes.

(continued on next page)

NAME | **DATE**

3-D Shape Hunt page 2 of 2

5 <u>CHALLENGE</u> Use some of the 3-D shapes you found to build new shapes and creations. If you have Legos, Duplos, or building blocks, make something new with them. Draw pictures of your creations on this sheet, or ask someone to take a picture of them to share with the class.

NAME _____ |DATE _____

 Addition, Subtraction & Shapes page 1 of 2

1 Add.

5	4	3	2	10	5
+ 5	+ 5	+ 7	+ 3	+ 0	+ 3

8	5	9	6	4	1
+ 2	+ 2	+ 1	+ 3	+ 6	+ 6

$3 + 4 + 2 =$ _____ $2 + 8 =$ _____ $2 + 3 + 5 =$ _____

2 Subtract.

9	10	8	10	9	10
− 2	− 3	− 8	− 1	− 3	− 5

10	7	10	10	9	10
− 2	− 3	− 8	− 7	− 5	− 10

$10 − 4 =$ _____ $10 − 6 =$ _____ $10 − 9 =$ _____

3 True or False? Circle one.

$3 + 4 = 8$	T	F	$9 = 3 + 4 + 2$	T	F
$7 = 5 + 4$	T	F	$1 + 2 + 7 = 10$	T	F
$2 + 3 + 3 = 10$	T	F	$8 = 3 + 5 + 0$	T	F
$9 − 3 = 5$	T	F	$8 − 5 = 2$	T	F
$10 − 4 = 6$	T	F	$10 − 8 = 3$	T	F

(continued on next page)

NAME | DATE

Addition, Subtraction & Shapes page 2 of 2

Mark the shape that does NOT belong with an X. Then explain why you think the shape does not belong.

4

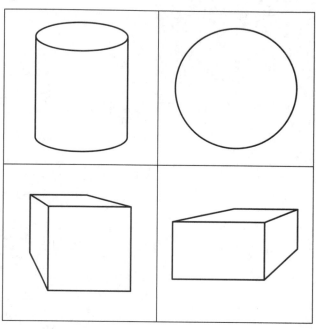

5

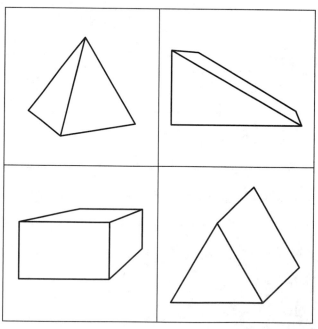

NAME _____ | DATE _____

🏠 Equations & Number Words page 1 of 2

1 Write an addition or subtraction equation that tells about the number of dark and light squares in each quilt block.

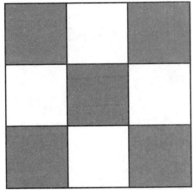 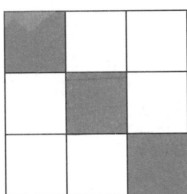 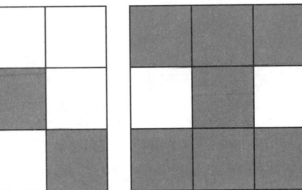

$$9 - 5 = 4$$

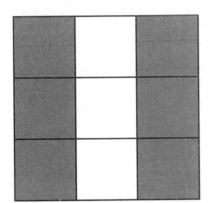 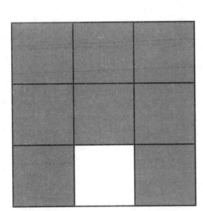 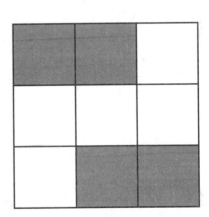

2 Solve the problems below:

4	2	3	1	9	6
+ 5	+ 7	+ 6	+ 8	+ 0	+ 3

9	9	9	9	9	9
− 5	− 0	− 3	− 7	− 2	− 4

(continued on next page)

NAME | DATE

Equations & Number Words page 2 of 2

3 Write an equation to match the dominoes. Then draw a line to the word that tells how many in all. You won't find a match for every word.

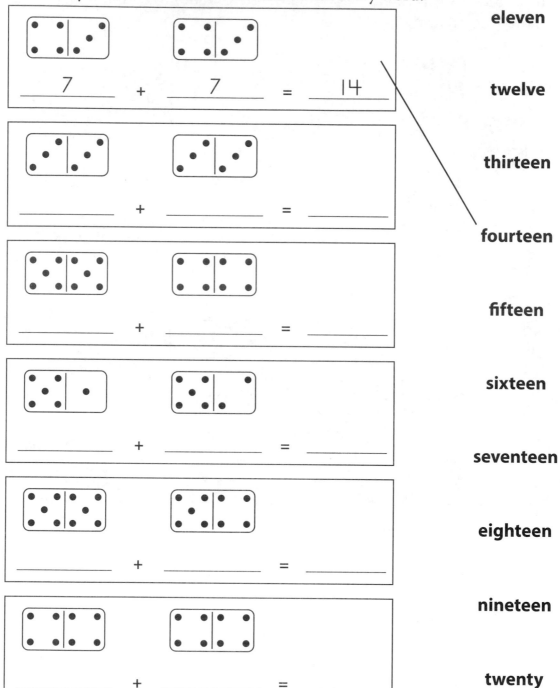

eleven

twelve

thirteen

fourteen

fifteen

sixteen

seventeen

eighteen

nineteen

twenty

80

NAME _____ | **DATE** _____

 Fractions, Halves & Doubles page 1 of 2

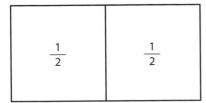 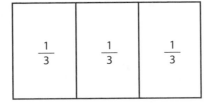 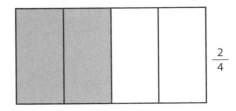

1 Draw lines to show two ways to cut a sandwich in half (2 equal parts). Label the parts.

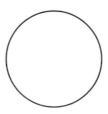

2 Draw lines to show how 4 people can share a pizza (4 equal parts). Label the parts.

3 These fraction cards are not colored in. Color the parts to show the fractions.

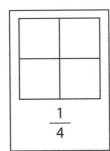 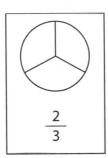

4 These fraction cards do not have a fraction written on them. Write the numbers to make the fraction.

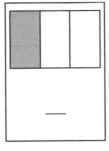 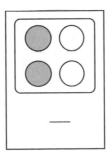

(continued on next page)

NAME _____ | DATE _____

Fractions, Halves & Doubles page 2 of 2

5 Add.

$4 + 4 =$ _____ $2 + 2 =$ _____ $10 + 10 =$ _____

$5 + 5 =$ _____ $6 + 6 =$ _____ $1 + 1 =$ _____

$3 + 3 =$ _____ $8 + 8 =$ _____ $11 + 11 =$ _____

$7 + 7 =$ _____ $9 + 9 =$ _____ $12 + 12 =$ _____

6 Subtract.

$8 - 4 =$ _____ $12 - 6 =$ _____ $20 - 10 =$ _____

$10 - 5 =$ _____ $18 - 9 =$ _____ $2 - 1 =$ _____

$14 - 7 =$ _____ $6 - 3 =$ _____ $1 - 0 =$ _____

$4 - 2 =$ _____ $16 - 8 =$ _____ $22 - 11 =$ _____

7 **CHALLENGE** Add and subtract.

70	90	60	200	400	300	1,000
+ 70	+ 90	+ 60	+ 200	+ 400	+ 300	+ 1,000

120	180	140	600	400	800	2,000
− 60	− 90	− 70	− 300	− 200	− 400	− 1,000

Shape Riddles & More page 1 of 2

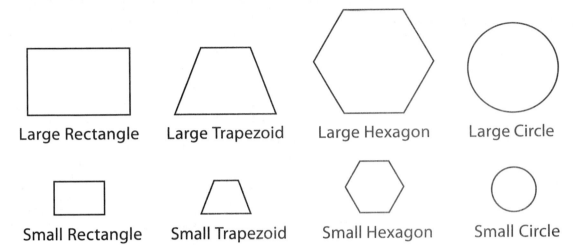

Large Rectangle   Large Trapezoid   Large Hexagon   Large Circle

Small Rectangle   Small Trapezoid   Small Hexagon   Small Circle

1   Read each set of clues to figure out which shape it will be. Draw the correct shape in the box.

Clues:	**Draw the shape.**
My shape has fewer than 6 sides.	
My shape has more than 3 sides.	
My shape is large.	
My shape has 2 slanted sides.	

Clues:	**Draw the shape.**
My shape has fewer than 6 sides.	
My shape is small.	
My shape does not have 4 sides.	
My shape does not have any straight sides.	

(continued on next page)

Shape Riddles & More page 2 of 2

2 Tim has 12 fish. Seven are yellow and the rest are red. How many red fish does Tim have? Show your work.

Tim has _____ red fish.

3 **CHALLENGE** Make a picture that is worth 36¢. You can only use these shapes. Label your picture. Prove that it is worth 36¢.

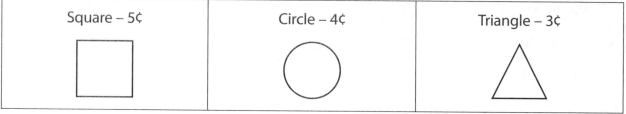

Square – 5¢	Circle – 4¢	Triangle – 3¢
□	○	△

Shapes, Fractions & Stories page 1 of 2

1 Color half of each shape below.

 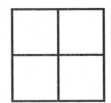 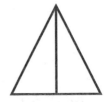

2 Solve the problems. Use the space to show your work.

a Luis and his sister Elisa like to count cars as they go by their house. Luis counted 10 yesterday and Elisa counted 7 today. How many cars did they count in all?

b Breanna saved 16 dimes. She spent 5 of them on stickers. How many dimes does she have left?

c Amira read for 11 minutes after school, 5 minutes after dinner, and another 4 minutes before she fell asleep. How many minutes did she read today?

(continued on next page)

Shapes, Fractions & Stories page 2 of 2

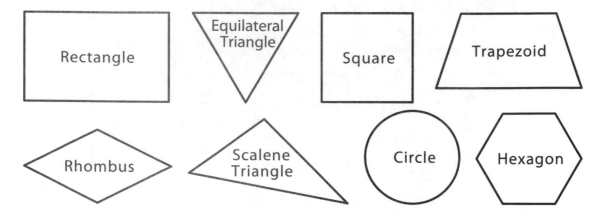

3 Solve the riddles below. Write the name of the shape in each box.

My shape has 4 corners. My shape has 4 equal sides. My shape is not a square. Can you guess my shape? It is a _____.	My shape has 3 sides. My shape has 3 corners. Each of its sides is a different length. Can you guess my shape? It is a _____.
My shape does not have 4 corners. My shape does not have 3 sides. My shape has no straight sides. Can you guess my shape? It is a _____.	My shape has more than 3 sides. My shape has more than 4 sides. My shape has 6 corners. Can you guess my shape? It is a _____.

NAME _____ | **DATE** _____

 Figure the Facts with Penguins page 1 of 2

1 Here is huddle of 10 penguins. Eight penguin pals are swimming toward the huddle so they can get warm too. How many penguins will there be in all when the 8 penguins join their friends? Write an equation beside the picture to show.

2 Here are 10 penguins in a huddle. Some more are coming to join them, and then there will be 13 penguins in the huddle. How many penguins are going to join the huddle? Fill in the empty box in the equation to show.

$$10 + \boxed{} = 13$$

3 **CHALLENGE** Write and solve your own penguin story problem. Make it fun, interesting, and challenging.

(continued on next page)

NAME _____ | DATE _____

Figure the Facts with Penguins page 2 of 2

4 Add.

5	4	3	2	10	5	2
$+5$	$+5$	$+7$	$+3$	$+0$	$+3$	$+2$

8	5	9	6	4	1	4
$+2$	$+2$	$+1$	$+3$	$+6$	$+6$	$+6$

$4 + 2 =$ _____ $2 + 3 + 5 =$ _____ $9 + 1 + 0 =$ _____

5 Subtract.

9	10	8	10	9	10	5
-8	-0	-4	-1	-3	-5	-4

10	7	10	8	6	10	7
-2	-3	-9	-7	-3	-10	-6

$6 - 4 =$ _____ $8 - 6 =$ _____ $10 - 9 =$ _____

6 $5 + 5$ is one way to make 10. $12 - 2$ is another way to make 10. Think of some other ways to make 10. Write at least 10 different ways to make 10.

NAME _____ | DATE _____

 Facts & Fish page 1 of 2

1 Write an equation to match each cube train.

ex

$$6 + 3 = 9$$

a

b

c

2 Color in the train to match the equation.

ex $3 + 6 = 9$

a $3 + 3 + 3 = 9$

b $7 + 2 = 9$

c $4 + 5 = 9$

3 Subtract.

$9 - 0 =$ _____ $9 - 3 =$ _____ $9 - 9 =$ _____ $9 - 2 =$ _____

$9 - 4 =$ _____ $9 - 1 =$ _____ $9 - 5 =$ _____ $9 - 8 =$ _____

$9 - 5 =$ _____ $9 - 3 =$ _____ $9 - 7 =$ _____ $9 - 6 =$ _____

4 Fill in the missing numbers.

$4 +$ _____ $= 9$ _____ $+ 6 = 9$ $9 = 7 +$ _____ $9 = 8 +$ _____

(continued on next page)

89

NAME _____ | DATE _____

Facts & Fish page 2 of 2

5 There are 12 fish in the tank. Five of the fish are blue. The rest of the fish are red. How many of the fish in the tank are red? Show your work.

_____ of the fish in the tank are red.

6 Jacob has 12 fish, and all of them are either yellow or red. There are twice as many yellow fish as red fish. How many yellow fish does Jacob have? How many red fish does Jacob have? Show your work.

Jacob has _____ yellow fish. Jacob has _____ red fish.

90

NAME _____ | **DATE** _____

 ## Double-Dot Cards for Eleven & Twelve page 1 of 2

1 Draw the dots on the right side of each card to make 11. Then write a fact family to match.

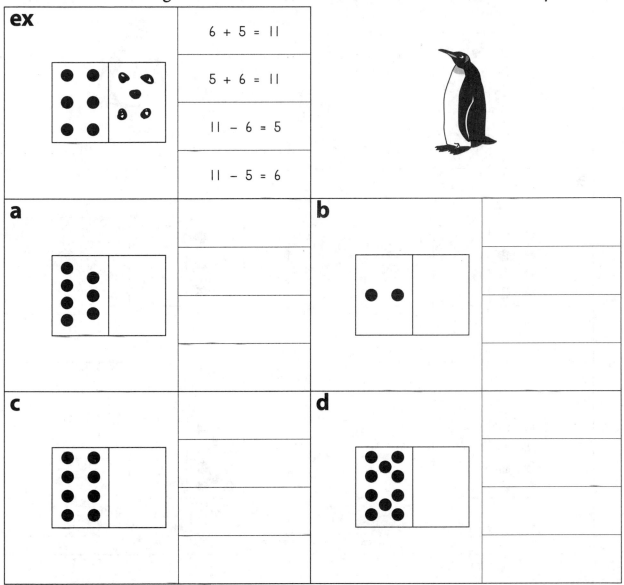

ex

6 + 5 = 11

5 + 6 = 11

11 – 6 = 5

11 – 5 = 6

a

b

c

d

2 Fill in the missing numbers.

9 + ☐ = 11	☐ + 1 = 11	5 + 6 = ☐	11 + ☐ = 11
11 – ☐ = 6	☐ – 1 = 10	11 – 4 = ☐	11 – ☐ = 8

(continued on next page)

91

NAME | **DATE**

Double-Dot Cards for Eleven & Twelve page 2 of 2

3 Draw the dots on the right side of each card to make 12. Then write a fact family to match.

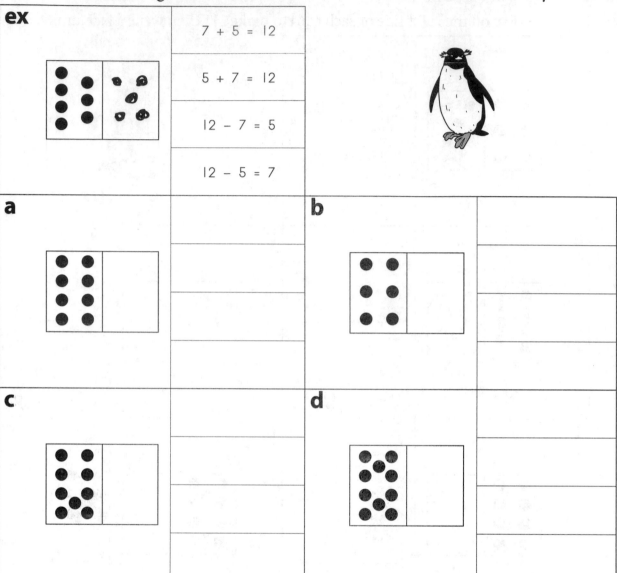

ex	
(dots)	7 + 5 = 12
	5 + 7 = 12
	12 − 7 = 5
	12 − 5 = 7

a		**b**	
(dots)		(dots)	

c		**d**	
(dots)		(dots)	

4 Fill in the missing numbers.

9 + ☐ = 12	☐ + 7 = 12	6 + 6 = ☐	12 + ☐ = 12
12 − ☐ = 0	☐ − 2 = 10	12 − 8 = ☐	12 − ☐ = 5

NAME _____ | DATE _____

 Combinations & Story Problems page 1 of 2

1 For each problem below:

• Circle the two numbers that make a total that is as close to 10 as possible. (If you don't find two that make 10 exactly, choose the two that come the closest, under or over.)

• Write an equation to match.

ex	④	5	⑥	4 + 6 = 10
a	3	4	7	___ + ___ = ___
b	8	2	6	___ + ___ = ___
c	9	5	1	___ + ___ = ___
d	7	4	8	___ + ___ = ___

2 For each problem below:

• Circle the two numbers that make a total that is as close to 20 as possible. (If you don't find two that make 20 exactly, choose the two that come the closest, under or over.)

• Write an equation to match.

ex	⑨	⑪	4	9 + 11 = 20
a	17	3	12	___ + ___ = ___
b	7	5	15	___ + ___ = ___
c	18	2	4	___ + ___ = ___
d	10	12	8	___ + ___ = ___

(continued on next page)

93

Combinations & Story Problems page 2 of 2

3 Rosa had 14 shells. She gave 3 of the shells to her sister and 4 of the shells to her brother. How many shells did Rosa have left? Show your work.

Rosa had _____ shells left.

4 Jared has 5 coins in his pocket. They are worth 18¢ in all. What coins does Jared have? Show your work.

Here are the 5 coins Jared has in his pocket:

NAME | DATE

 Penguin Problem Solving page 1 of 2

Read and solve each of the problems below. Show your work.

- Use numbers, pictures, or words to help solve the problem.
- Fill in the missing number in the equation when you find the answer.

1   Five penguins are on the ice. Six penguins in the water. How many penguins in all?

$5 + 6 = \boxed{}$ penguins

2   There are 8 penguins on the ice and some more penguins in the water. There are 11 penguins in all. How many penguins are in the water?

$8 + \boxed{} = 11$ penguins

3   There are 13 penguins in all. Seven of them are in the water. How many penguins are hiding behind the hill?

$\boxed{} + 7 = 13$ penguins

(continued on next page)

NAME _____ **| DATE** _____

Penguin Problem Solving page 2 of 2

4 There were 13 penguins standing on the ice. Three dove into the water. How many penguins were left on the ice?

13 – 3 = ☐ penguins

5 There were 12 penguins standing on the ice. Some of the penguins dove into the water. Now there are only 3 penguins left on the ice. How many penguins dove in?

12 – ☐ = 3 penguins

6 **CHALLENGE** Some penguins were playing on the ice. Ten of them dove into the water. A few seconds later, 6 of those penguins jumped back onto the ice. Now there are 12 penguins on the ice. How many penguins were on the ice to start? Use numbers, pictures, or words to show how you got the answer.

NAME | DATE

 Equations & Fact Practice page 1 of 2

1 Circle T if the equation is true. Circle F if the equation is false.

ex $10 + 3 = 13$	T	F	**a** $6 + 6 = 12$	T	F
b $12 = 7 + 5$	T	F	**c** $12 - 8 = 4$	T	F
d $10 - 2 = 6$	T	F	**e** $10 = 6 + 4$	T	F
f $5 + 6 = 6 + 5$	T	F	**g** $11 = 3 + 7$	T	F

2 Read the story. Circle T if it could be true. Circle F if it must be false.

a Sara had 8 cars. She got 7 more cars for her birthday.   T   F
Now she has 15 cars in all.

b Max made 13 cookies. His brother ate all the cookies.   T   F
Max has 3 cookies left.

3 Read the story. Circle the matching equation.

a There were 4 bugs in the garden, and then 9 more bugs came. How many bugs in all?

$13 - 4 = 9$ $10 + 3 = 13$ $4 + 4 = 8$ $4 + 9 = 13$

b Fourteen frogs were in the pond. Then 6 frogs hopped away. How many frogs were left?

$14 + 6 = 20$ $14 - 6 = 8$ $14 - 4 = 10$ $12 - 6 = 6$

c There were 12 penguins standing on the ice and 2 penguins in the water. How many more penguins were there on the ice than in the water?

$12 + 2 = 14$ $2 + 8 = 10$ $12 - 2 = 10$ $14 - 12 = 2$

(continued on next page)

NAME _____ | DATE _____

Equations & Fact Practice page 2 of 2

4 Solve each problem below.

a

$10 + 4 =$ _____

b

$9 + 4 =$ _____

c

$10 + 6 =$ _____

d

$9 + 6 =$ _____

e

$10 + 8 =$ _____

f

$9 + 8 =$ _____

5 Fill in the blanks.

$10 + 0 =$ _____

$9 + 0 =$ _____

$10 + 3 =$ _____

$9 + 3 =$ _____

$10 + 1 =$ _____

$9 + 1 =$ _____

$10 + 7 =$ _____

$9 + 7 =$ _____

$10 + 2 =$ _____

$9 + 2 =$ _____

$10 + 5 =$ _____

$9 + 5 =$ _____

$10 + 9 =$ _____

$9 + 9 =$ _____

$4 + 10 =$ _____

$4 + 9 =$ _____

$6 + 10 =$ _____

$6 + 9 =$ _____

$8 + 10 =$ _____

$8 + 9 =$ _____

$10 +$ _____ $= 17$

$9 +$ _____ $= 17$

NAME _____ | DATE _____

 Penguins & Fact Practice page 1 of 2

1 Add.

5	4	3	2	10	5	7
+ 5	+ 5	+ 7	+ 3	+ 0	+ 3	+ 2

8	5	9	6	4	2	4
+ 2	+ 2	+ 1	+ 3	+ 6	+ 6	+ 3

3 + 4 + 2 = _____   2 + 3 + 5 = _____   1 + 2 + 3 + 4 = _____

2 Subtract.

9	10	8	10	9	10	9
− 5	− 0	− 4	− 1	− 3	− 5	− 4

10	7	10	10	10	10	9
− 2	− 3	− 8	− 7	− 3	− 10	− 7

10 − 4 = _____   10 − 6 = _____   10 − 9 = _____   9 − 6 = _____

3 There were 5 penguins behind the hill, 4 penguins on the ice, and 10 penguins in the water. How many penguins in all?

There were _____ penguins in all.

(continued on next page)

Penguins & Fact Practice page 2 of 2

**See how many penguins are standing on the ice?
Half as many are swimming in the water.
How many are swimming? How many penguins in all?**

4 Show how you solve the problem with pictures, numbers, and words.

There are _____ penguins swimming.

There are _____ penguins in all.

NAME _____ | DATE _____

 Skip-Counting by Twos & Threes page 1 of 2

1 Fill in the missing numbers.

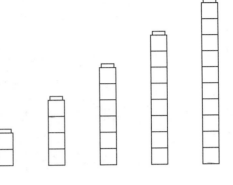

1	2	3	4	5	6	7	8	9	10
11	12	13		15	16	17		19	20
21		23	24	25		27	28	29	
31	32	33		35	36	37		39	40
41		43	44	45		47	48	49	

a Write the missing numbers on the line.

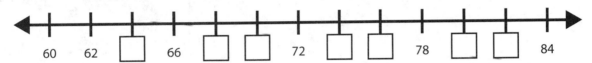

60   62   ☐   66   ☐   ☐   72   ☐   ☐   78   ☐   ☐   84

2 Fill in the missing numbers.

1	2	3	4	5	6	7	8	9	10
11	12		14	15	16		18	19	20
	22	23	24		26	27	28		30
31	32		34	35	36		38	39	40
	42	43	44		46	47	48		50

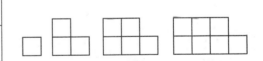

a Write the missing numbers on the line.

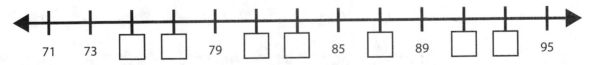

71   73   ☐   ☐   79   ☐   ☐   85   ☐   89   ☐   ☐   95

3 Solve the problems below.

34 + 2 = _____   44 + 2 = _____   26 + 2 = _____

11 + 2 = _____   17 + 2 = _____   43 + 2 = _____

(continued on next page)

Skip-Counting by Twos & Threes page 2 of 2

4 How many penguins in each row?

one family

two families

three families

four families

five families

5 Fill in the numbers.

1	2		4	5		7	8		10
11		13	14		16	17		19	20
	22	23		25	26		28	29	
	32		34	35		37	38		40
41		43	44		46	47		49	50

Fifty or Bust! page 1 of 3

Note to Families

In this game, players practice adding 10 and another number. The boxes on the playing cards and the record sheet are arranged in tens to make counting, adding, and coloring easier. You can show your child how quickly you can add and color the combinations by counting a stack of 10 first and then adding the ones.

Materials

- Fifty or Bust! pages 1–3
- crayons in 4 or 5 different colors

Instructions

1 Cut out the cards on page 3. Mix them up and place them face-down in a pile.

2 Pick a card, add the amount shown, and color in that many small boxes on your side of the record sheet (page 2). Work from left to right and bottom to top.

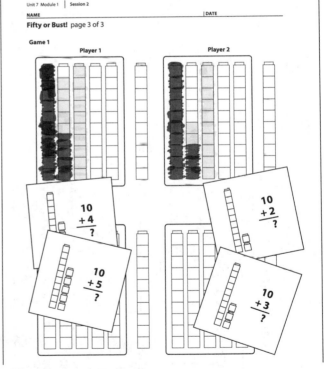

3 Have your partner take a turn and do the same.

4 Each of you take another turn. Use a different color this time. (Color the 5 stacks inside the box first; the stack outside the box is used only if a player goes bust.)

- Who has more now?
- How many more do you each need to get to 50?

5 Continue to take cards if you think you will not go over 50. Is there a card that would get you closer to 50 without going over?

- You can stop taking cards at any time.
- The winner is the player who gets closest to 50 without going over.

6 Play the game again, now or later. Save the cards for practicing facts at home.

(continued on next page)

Fifty or Bust! page 2 of 3

Record Sheet

Game 1

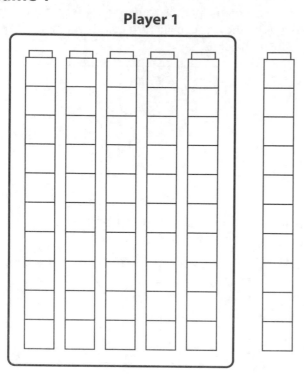

Player 1

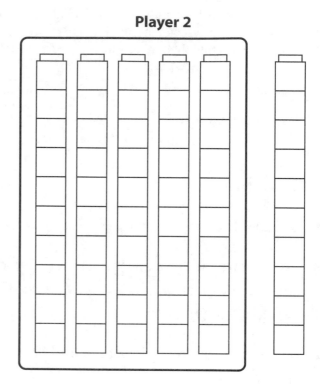

Player 2

Game 2

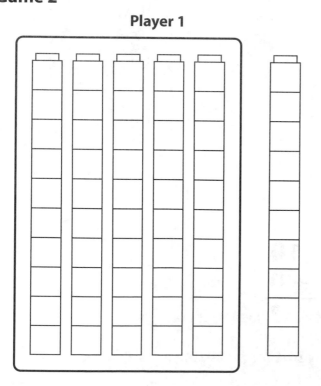

Player 1

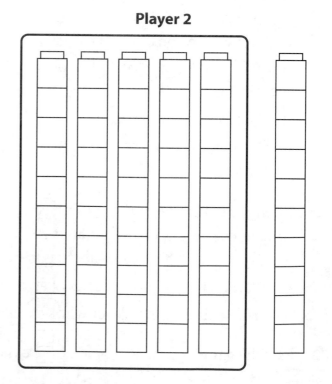

Player 2

(continued on next page)

104

Fifty or Bust! page 3 of 3

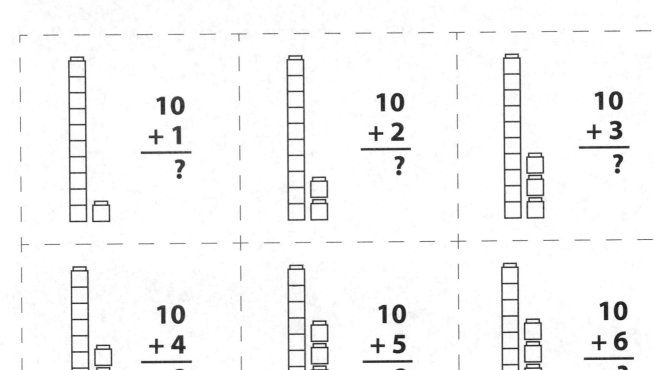

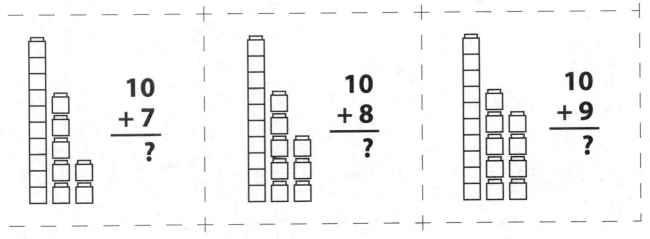

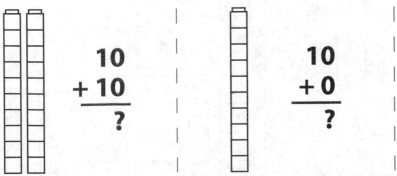

$$\begin{array}{r} 10 \\ +\ 1 \\ \hline ? \end{array}$$

$$\begin{array}{r} 10 \\ +\ 2 \\ \hline ? \end{array}$$

$$\begin{array}{r} 10 \\ +\ 3 \\ \hline ? \end{array}$$

$$\begin{array}{r} 10 \\ +\ 4 \\ \hline ? \end{array}$$

$$\begin{array}{r} 10 \\ +\ 5 \\ \hline ? \end{array}$$

$$\begin{array}{r} 10 \\ +\ 6 \\ \hline ? \end{array}$$

$$\begin{array}{r} 10 \\ +\ 7 \\ \hline ? \end{array}$$

$$\begin{array}{r} 10 \\ +\ 8 \\ \hline ? \end{array}$$

$$\begin{array}{r} 10 \\ +\ 9 \\ \hline ? \end{array}$$

$$\begin{array}{r} 10 \\ +\ 10 \\ \hline ? \end{array}$$

$$\begin{array}{r} 10 \\ +\ 0 \\ \hline ? \end{array}$$

🏠 **Solving Problems** page 1 of 2

1 Add.

10 + 5 = _____   10 + 9 = _____   10 + 2 = _____   10 + 10 = _____

20 + 4 = _____   50 + 1 = _____   30 + 7 = _____   70 + 3 = _____

2 Add.

30	40	20	30	60	30	70
+ 10	+ 10	+ 20	+ 20	+ 10	+ 30	+ 20

3 Color the ten-stacks to find out how much is left. Fill in the numbers on the number strip.

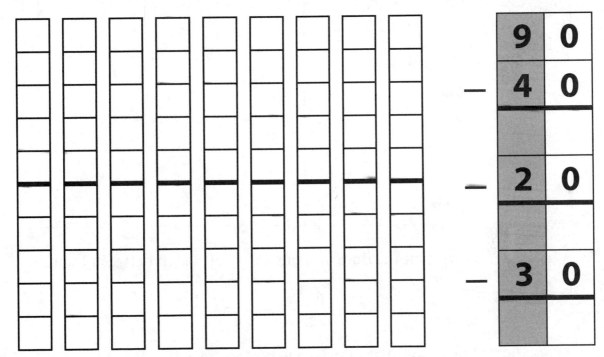

4 Subtract.

2 – 1 = _____   20 – 10 = _____   4 – 2 = _____   40 – 20 = _____

6 – 3 = _____   60 – 30 = _____   8 – 4 = _____   80 – 40 = _____

10 – 5 = _____   100 – 50 = _____   12 – 6 = _____   120 – 60 = _____

(continued on next page)

NAME _____ | DATE _____

Solving Problems page 2 of 2

5 Sasha has 47 Popsicle sticks (4 bundles of 10 and 7 sticks), and Jose has 62 (6 bundles of 10 and 2 sticks).

a Sketch Sasha's sticks in the first box and Jose's in the second box. (Hint: Use a rectangle for each bundle and a line for each stick.)

Sasha's Sticks	Jose's Sticks

b Write the numbers on the lines and put a >, <, or = sign between them.

_____ ◯ _____

c **CHALLENGE** How many sticks do Sasha and Jose have in all? _____
Show how you know with sketches, numbers, or words.

NAME _____ | DATE _____

🏠 Counting More Pebbles Along the Path page 1 of 2

Look at the pebbles along each part of the path. Fill in the missing numbers.

1

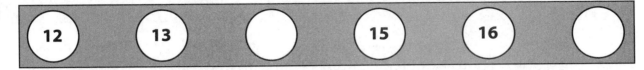

a **CHALLENGE** Hansel and Gretel used a pebble to mark every 10 steps as they walked along the path. How many steps have they taken when they get to the last pebble on this part of the path? _____ Use numbers or words to explain how you know.

2

3

(continued on next page)

NAME _____ | DATE _____

Counting More Pebbles Along the Path page 2 of 2

4

a **CHALLENGE** Hansel and Gretel used a pebble to mark every 10 steps as they walked along the path. How many steps have they taken when they get to the last pebble on this part of the path? _____ Use numbers or words to explain how you know.

b **CHALLENGE** How many more pebbles will Hansel and Gretel need to drop after the last one on this part of the path to mark the 1000th step they take? _____ Use numbers or words to explain how you figured it out.

5

6

Paths & Fives Practice page 1 of 2

1 Hansel and Gretel marked the paths around their house in the woods with pebbles so they could find their way back home. Here is a path for you to mark.

- Choose a starting number between 0 and 50 for your path, and write it in the Starting Number box.

- Choose two different objects (like pebbles, pinecones, or any other small objects you choose) to mark your path. Draw at least 7 of each on your path.

- Fill in the key to show the number of steps each object marks (see example).

- Write a number under 10 of the objects on your path to show how many steps it would take to get to each of them.

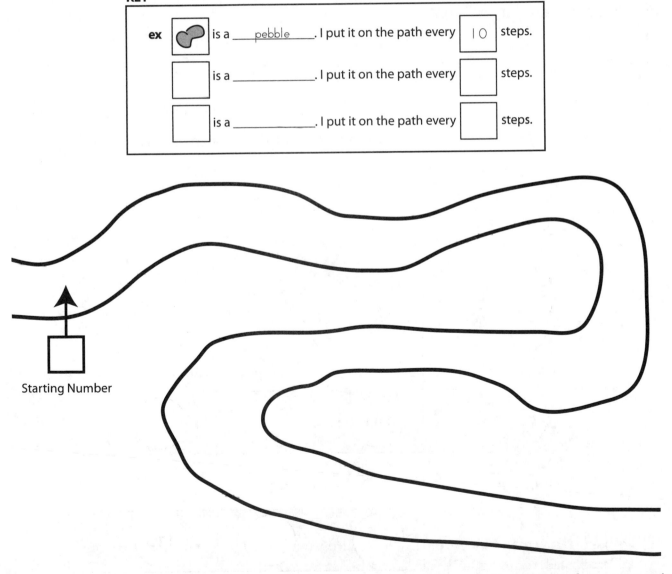

KEY

ex ⬭ is a ___pebble___. I put it on the path every | 10 | steps.

⬜ is a _____. I put it on the path every ⬜ steps.

⬜ is a _____. I put it on the path every ⬜ steps.

Starting Number

(continued on next page)

NAME | DATE

Paths & Fives Practice page 2 of 2

2 Write the 5s counting pattern to 70 under the ten-frames below. The first three numbers have been done for you.

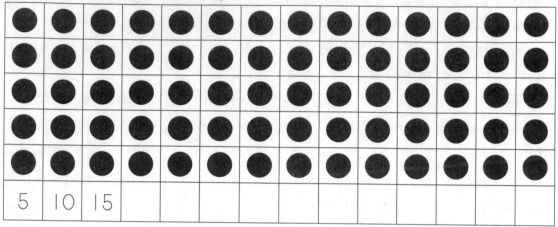

| 5 | 10 | 15 | | | | | | | | | | | |

3 Practicing adding and subtracting 5s.

20	35	10	0	5	45	25
+ 5	+ 5	+ 5	+ 5	+ 5	+ 5	+ 5

15	30	25	5	50	20	10
− 5	− 5	− 5	− 5	− 5	− 5	− 5

4 Fill in the blanks.

5 feet. How many toes in all?
_____

6 hands. How many fingers in all? _____

4 feet. How many toes in all?
_____

9 hands. How many fingers in all? _____

45 toes. How many feet?
_____

35 fingers. How many hands?
_____

NAME _____ | DATE _____

 Dots, Patterns, Blocks & Apples page 1 of 2

1 Fill in the missing numbers to complete the addition facts.

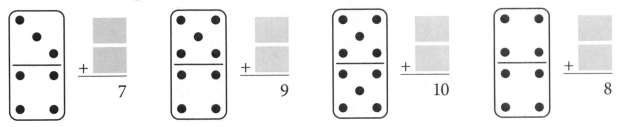

2 Fill in the missing dots and numbers to complete the addition facts.

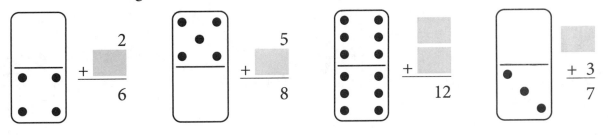

3 Make up your own combinations for these numbers. Fill in the dots and numbers.

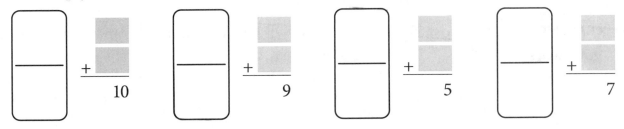

4 Fill in the missing numbers to complete the pattern.

a Skip-count by 2s.

22, 24, 26, _____, _____, _____

b Skip-count by 2s.

27, 29, 31, _____, _____, _____

c Skip-count down by 2s.

19, 17, 15, _____, 11, _____

d Skip-count down by 2s.

43, 41, _____, _____, 35

(continued on next page)

NAME _____ | **DATE** _____

Dots, Patterns, Blocks & Apples page 2 of 2

5 Rosa has 6 blocks. Eric has 7 more blocks than Rosa. How many blocks does Eric have? Show your work.

Eric has _____ blocks.

6 **CHALLENGE** 4 apples cost $1.00. How much will Jenny have to pay for 5 apples? Show your work.

Jenny will have to pay _____ for 5 apples.

114

NAME _____ | DATE _____

 Path Practice page 1 of 2

Answer the questions about each path. Remember that each fence section is 10 steps long, each bench is 5 steps long, and each flowerpot is 1 step long.

1 The fence on this path begins at step 32.

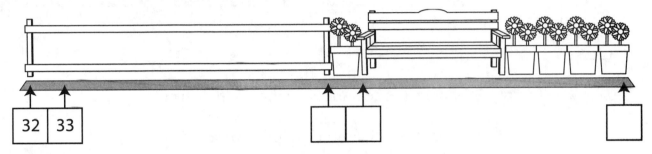

32	33

a What number belongs in the box at the end of the fence? _____

b What number belongs in the box at the beginning of the bench? _____

c What number belongs in the box below the last flowerpot? _____

2 The first fence section on this path begins at step 53.

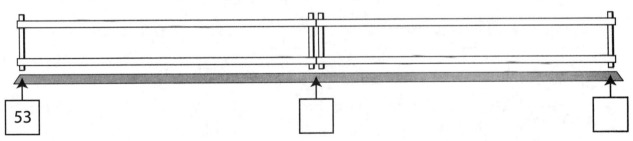

53

a What number belongs in the box at the end of the first fence section? _____

b What number belongs in the box at the end of the second fence section? _____

(continued on next page)

NAME _____ | DATE _____

Path Practice page 2 of 2

3 The first flowerpot on this path is set on step 19.

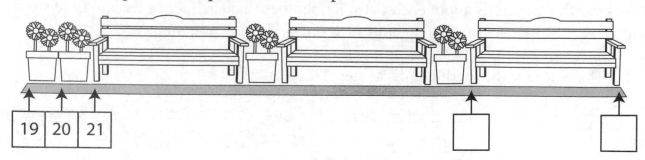

| 19 | 20 | 21 |

a What number belongs in the box below the last flowerpot? _____

b What number belongs in the box at end of the last bench? _____

4 Fill in the boxes with the correct numbers. Remember that each fence section is 10 steps long, each bench is 5 steps long, and each flowerpot is 1 step long.

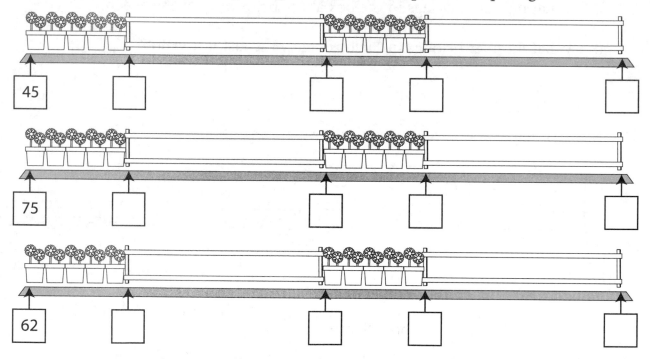

45

75

62

5 **CHALLENGE** Write a story problem to match the equation in the box. Then solve your own problem and write the answer.

$42 + 23 = \boxed{}$

NAME | DATE

 Coins & Clocks page 1 of 2

Sarah made a graph about the coins in her piggy bank.

1 How many pennies does Sarah have?

2 How many nickels does Sarah have?

3 Which coin does Sarah have the most of?

4 Which coin does Sarah have the fewest of?

5 **CHALLENGE** Count all the money on the graph. How much is there in all?

Coins in Sarah's Piggy Bank

	dimes	nickels	pennies
6			penny
5		nickel	penny
4	dime	nickel	penny
3	dime	nickel	penny
2	dime	nickel	penny
1	dime	nickel	penny

6 Write three observations about Sarah's coin collection:

(continued on next page)

Coins & Clocks page 2 of 2

7 Draw lines to connect the clocks that show the same time.

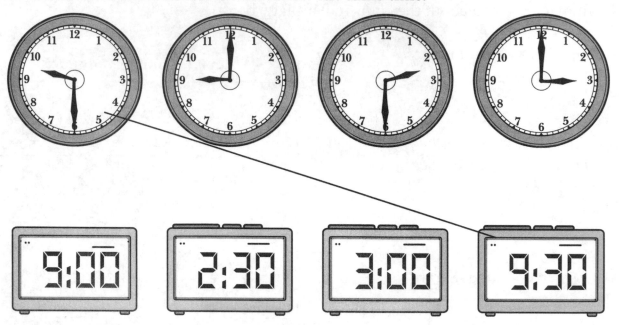

8 Draw the hour hand and minute hand to match the times below each clock.

NAME _____ | DATE _____

 Coins & More Coins page 1 of 2

Penny 1¢   **Nickel 5¢**   **Dime 10¢**

Trace the numbers and words. Then draw a line to the matching set of coins and fill in the correct amount of money. One number does not have a matching set.

ex    20 ____ ¢    10 ten

1    _____ ¢   20 twenty

2 _____ ¢   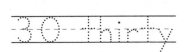 30 thirty

3     _____ ¢   40 forty

4 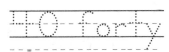   _____ ¢   50 fifty

5      _____ ¢   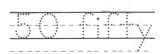 60 sixty

6    _____ ¢   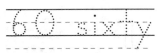 70 seventy

              _____ ¢

              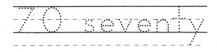 80 eighty

(continued on next page)

Coins & More Coins page 2 of 2

7 Use the coordinates below to figure out which coins you capture. Then count how much money you won.

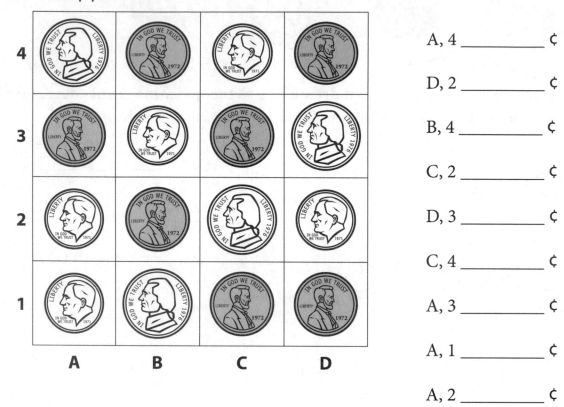

A, 4 _____ ¢

D, 2 _____ ¢

B, 4 _____ ¢

C, 2 _____ ¢

D, 3 _____ ¢

C, 4 _____ ¢

A, 3 _____ ¢

A, 1 _____ ¢

A, 2 _____ ¢

8 How much money did you win? Show how you figured it out:

I won _____ ¢

NAME | **DATE**

 Race You to 25¢ page 1 of 3

Note to Families

This game involves counting and comparing money, as well as "regrouping"—trading in 5 pennies for a nickel and 5 nickels for a quarter. Students have been counting pennies, nickels, and dimes in class.

Materials

- Race You to 25¢ pages 1–3
- 30 pennies, 10 nickels, and 2 quarters
- a pencil and a paperclip to make a spinner

Instructions

1 Before you play, practice trading coins. Count 5 pennies and trade them for a nickel. Count nickels by 5s (5, 10, 15, 20, 25) and trade them for a quarter.

2 Use the paperclip and the pencil to make a spinner.

3 Take turns spinning and setting the coins on your board. (For example, if you spin 3¢, you set 3 pennies on top of the pictures of pennies on your board.)

4 When you have 5 or more pennies, trade them in for a nickel. (Any extras stay on the board.) When you finally collect 5 nickels, trade them in for a quarter.

5 The first person to get a quarter wins the game!

6 If you make a rule that a person has to reach 25¢ exactly, it allows the other player to catch up and makes things a little more fun.

7 Play the game several times over the next few days.

(continued on next page)

NAME

DATE

Race You to 25¢ page 2 of 3

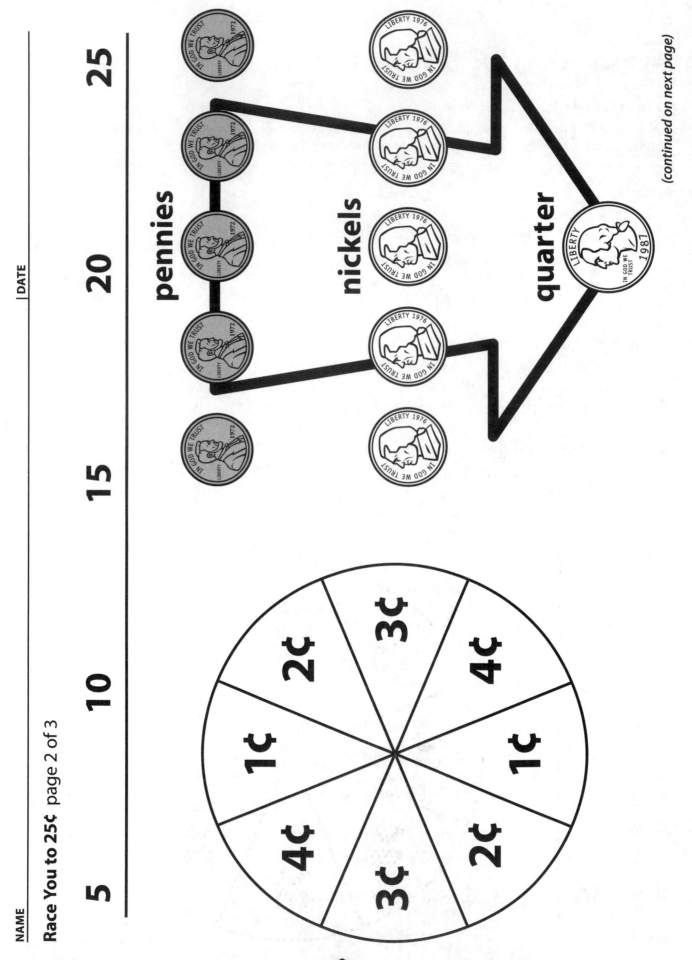

pennies

nickels

quarter

5   10   15   20   25

1¢ 2¢ 3¢ 4¢ 1¢ 2¢ 3¢ 4¢

(continued on next page)

NAME | DATE

Race You to 25¢ page 3 of 3

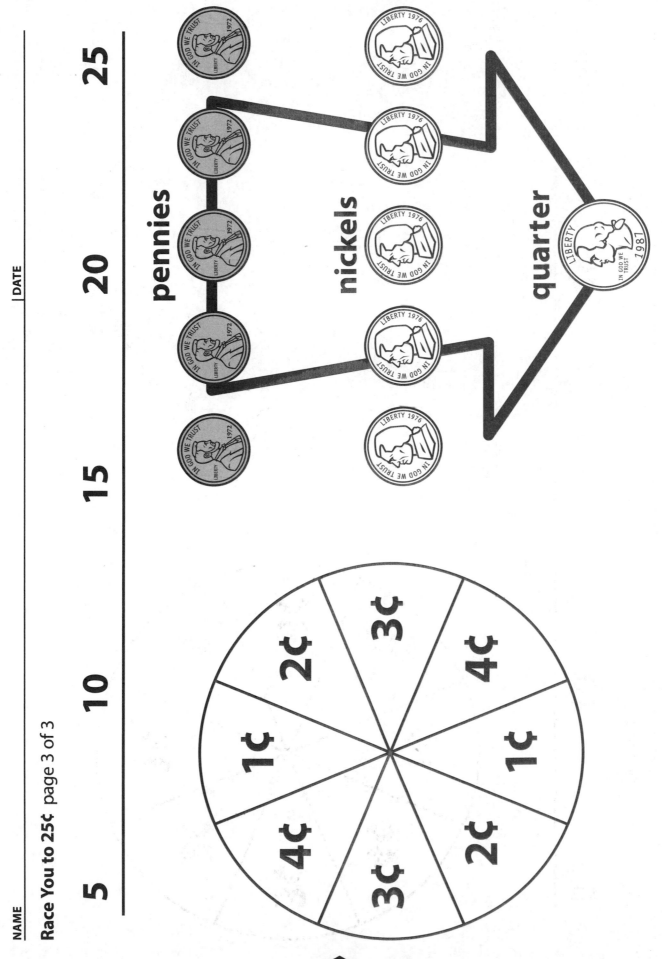

NAME _____ | **DATE** _____

 Danny's School Day page 1 of 2

This is Danny. He goes to school every day except Saturday and Sunday.

1 At 8:00, Danny gets on the bus. Circle the clock that says 8:00.

2 At 10:00, Danny's class goes to recess. Circle the clock that says 10:00.

3 At 11:30, Danny's class does math. Circle the clock that says 11:30.

4 At 12:30, Danny's class goes to lunch. Circle the clock that says 12:30.

5 At 1:00, Danny's class has Story Time. Circle the clock that says 1:00.

NAME |DATE

Danny's School Day page 2 of 2

Here are some other times in Danny's school day. Draw lines to connect the clocks that tell the same time.

School Starts

Reading Time

Writing Time

P.E.

Science Time

School Ends

126

NAME _____ | DATE _____

 Facts & Questions page 1 of 2

A story problem gives you some facts and asks a question. For each problem on this page:

- Underline the facts.
- Put a box around the question.
- Solve the problem and show your work.
- Write the answer on the line.

ex <u>There were 10 army ants. Three went out to get some food.</u> How many ants were left?

$$10 - 3 = 7$$

There were __7__ ants left.

1 Six ants are working hard. Some more come to help. Now there are 13 ants. How many ants came to help?

_____ ants came to help.

2 There are 7 ants at the top of the tunnel. There are 4 ants in the middle chamber. There are 5 ants in the lower chamber. How many ants in all?

There are _____ ants in all.

3 There are 6 ants. Each ant has 3 seeds. How many seeds in all?

There are _____ seeds in all.

(continued on next page)

NAME _____ | DATE _____

Facts & Questions page 2 of 2

4 James had 17 baseball cards. He gave 9 of them to Andre. Who has more baseball cards now, James or Andre? How many more? Show your work.

_____ has _____ more baseball card(s) than _____.

5 **CHALLENGE** Teri went to the school store. She gave the clerk a $1 bill. She got 30¢ back in change. What might she have bought? Find three possible answers. Show your work.

School Store Price List	
Markers	25¢ each
Tablets	30¢ each
Erasers	10¢ each
Pencils	20¢ each
Folders	15¢ each

My, How We've Grown!

Note to Families

As we come close to the end of our first grade year, we can look back and see all of the ways we have changed —not just this year, but all through our lives. Help your child discover and record these changes.

How have I changed?

Think about all the ways in which you have changed since you were born. Do you look different? Can you do things now that you couldn't then? Write at least 10 ways you have changed.

ex I'm much taller! _____

1 _____

2 _____

3 _____

4 _____

5 _____

6 _____

7 _____

8 _____

9 _____

10 _____

_____

_____

_____

_____

(continued on next page)

NAME _____ |**DATE** _____

My, How We've Grown! page 2 of 2

Note to Families

How long was your child at birth? You might find this information in a baby book, on a hospital card or certificate, on a wristband, or on a report from the doctor or health clinic. If you cannot find this information, make a good estimate. The average length of a full-term baby born in the United States is about 20 inches.

Materials

- My, How We've Grown! pages 1 & 2
- piece of string, yarn, or ribbon
- measuring tape or ruler
- scissors
- masking tape (or use some at school)

How have I grown?

One of the ways you have changed since you were born is that you are much bigger. Ask an adult how long you were when you were born.

1 I was _____ inches long when I was born.

2 Use a measuring tape or ruler to see how long you were.

3 Measure your piece of string, yarn, or ribbon to match your length when you were born.

4 Cut the string.

5 Write your name on a piece of masking tape and attach it to the string. (If you don't have masking tape, you can do this part at school.)

6 Bring your string back to school so you can compare with other students.

NAME _____ | DATE _____

 My Timeline

Note to Families

Now that your child has been thinking about how they've grown and changed over the years, it's time to make a timeline of their life. You can help them think of an important event from each year of their life, and to find photos to represent each event (or have them draw pictures if you don't have the photos).

Materials

- My Timeline Home Connection page
- 7 photos, 1 for each year of your life [OR] drawings or magazine pictures
- tape or glue, depending on whether you want to remove the pictures later or not

Instructions

A lot has happened to you since you were born!

1 Think about the important things that have happened. Can you think of one thing from each year? You might want to include your birth, when you started school, and other important events in your life (like moving to a new town, going on a great vacation, learning to ride a bike, starting to walk, having a new baby or pet in your family, etc.).

2 Have an adult help you collect a photo for each event, or help you draw a picture or cut one out of a magazine.

3 Put the first picture in the first empty space on your timeline. Use tape or glue. Leave room under the picture for a caption.

Kendra's Timeline	0–1	2	3	4	5	6	7

4 Write a caption under the picture. For example, if the picture is of you when you were born, you could write, "I was born July 10, 20___."

5 Continue placing or drawing a picture in each space, and writing a caption underneath.

6 Bring your timeline back to school.

NAME | DATE

Glider Flights & Clocks page 2 of 2

5 Read each of these clock faces and write the time on the digital clock.

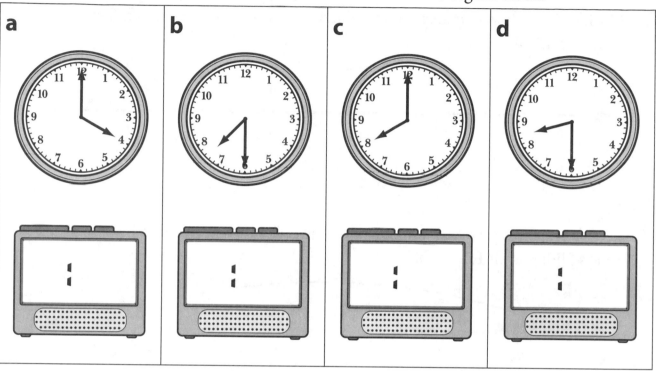

a　　**b**　　**c**　　**d**

6 Read each of these digital clocks and mark the time on the clock face.

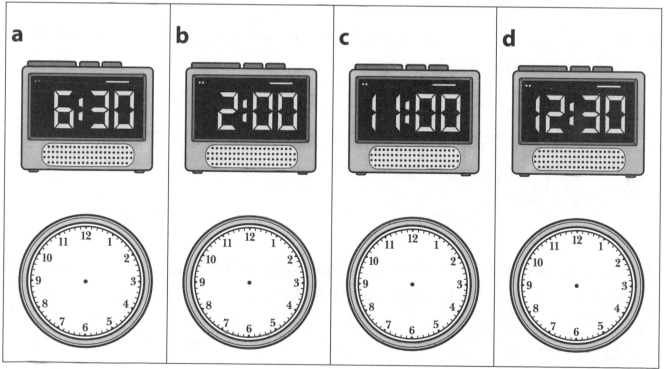

a　　**b**　　**c**　　**d**

Glider Flights & Clocks page 1 of 2

1 Mark's glider flew 45 cubes. Maya's glider flew 60 cubes. How much farther did Maya's plane fly?

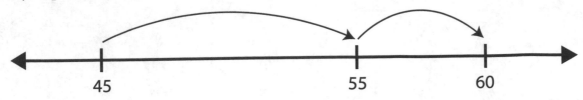

45   55   60

2 Jason's glider flew 54 cubes. Kyle's glider flew 10 more cubes than Jason's. Where did Kyle's glider land? Fill in the circle.

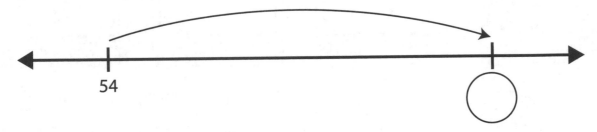

54

3 Sandro's glider landed at 72. Shawna's glider landed 20 less than Sandro's. Where did Shawna's glider land?

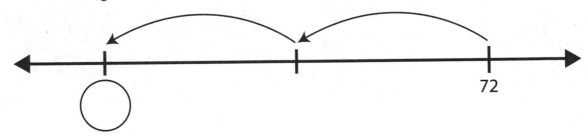

72

4 Nico's first flight went 30 cubes. His second flight went 65. Mark both flights on the number line. How much longer is his second flight?

(continued on next page)